Advances in Chemistry Series

Robert F. Gould, ***Editor***

AMERICAN CHEMICAL SOCIETY

APPLIED PUBLICATIONS

CONTENTS

INTRODUCTION

For a number of years, the mass spectrometer has been applied to the elucidation of problems in molecular structure. Correlations of mass spectra with structure have now been made for almost all of the common types of organic compounds *(2, 8)*. Most of these correlations by necessity, emphasize the type of spectral pattern or decomposition paths to be expected for a particular type of molecular structure. However, in determining the structure of an unknown compound, the reverse situation is presented — i. e., the prominent ions in the mass spectrum are known, from which one wishes to determine the most probable molecular structure or structures. When the reference mass spectrum of the unknown has been run previously, this can be located from the prominent peaks, using a number of filing systems previously described *(5, 6, 9, 11, 14, 15)*. However, it obviously is highly desirable to have an identification system not dependent on the availability of the standard spectrum of the unknown. This similar problem in other fields of spectroscopy has led to charts or tables indicating the prominent functional groups or other structural features which are found at particular wave lengths. Perhaps such tabulations have been most widely used in infrared spectroscopy — e.g., "the Colthup chart" *(4)*. A previous suggestion for such a system for mass spectrometry *(9)* has led to the accompanying tabulation of mass spectral correlations.

GENERAL DESCRIPTION

In designing this table, the purpose was to provide, where possible, the empirical and structural formulas of ions that might be found at a particular *m/e* in a mass spectrum, plus an indication of how each such ion might have arisen. A further purpose was to give an indication of the probability of each such classification of ions occurring. Thus, the table should indicate possible ion structures and precursor molecules for each of the prominent ions in the mass spectrum of an unknown compound, with a further indication of the general probability of their occurrence.

The mass spectral data used in this tabulation were available in a card file *(9)* containing a card for each of the 10 most prominent peaks in the 4000 referenced mass spectra. These cards were filed serially by nominal mass number with separation within each *m/e* by order of abundance in the particular mass spectrum. Thus, at *m/e* 123 in this file there appeared a card for each compound in which *m/e* 123 was one of the 10 most abundant ions in the mass spectrum. Cards for all compounds in which *m/e* 123 was the largest peak in the spectrum appeared first, followed by those in which *m/e* 123 was the second largest, etc., through the 10th most abundant.

To prepare the tabular correlation, each of the cards filed under a particular mass number was examined to ascertain the relationship of this peak in the spectrum to the structure of the compound. Where possible, the empirical and structural formulas and the mechanism of formation of the ion were assigned, plus the general structural type or functional group of the particular compound which gave rise to this ion. The number of cards under each such classification under the particular *m/e* were recorded for each magnitude (second most abundant, etc.). Such data were accumulated for the three most abundant ions in all mass numbers filed (*m/e* 1-500), with less abundant ions being included for those mass numbers containing fewer cards in the three highest peaks. All 10 of the highest peaks in the spectra were included above *m/e* 218.

Some ions were not included in the classifications because it was felt that they were not sufficiently representative of types of compound structures or functional groups. These are listed as the "P.I.D. ions," representing the "*Parent*" or molecular ions, ions due to *isotopic* species of smaller or artificial abundance — e.g., carbon-13 or deuterium — and *doubly* charged (or multiply charged) ions or other ions of fractional mass, as metastable ions. "Other unclassified" ions are those for which it was felt there was insufficient evidence of their structural significance for classification.

PRESENTATION OF DATA

m/e. The mass-to-charge ratio in the first column of the table is calculated from the assumed empirical formula, using the atomic weight scale based on carbon = 12.000000. Almost all of the spectra used in this study, however, were run on instruments of insufficient resolving power to determine such fractional masses, so that it had to be assumed that each peak represented only one empirical formula. Thus, the significant figures shown are as calculated, not as determined. The correlations should still prove useful, however, where it is possible to determine the *m/e* of the unknown peak in question to millmass unit accuracies. As has been shown extensively by Beynon and coworkers *(1, 2)*, this will then make possible the assignment of the empirical formula within each of the unit mass classifications, and thus simplify the identification problem.

There is a definite possibility that even the nominal mass number is in error, because of the very large number of spectra examined and the "uncertified" nature of these. This is especially true, naturally, at higher mass numbers, where resolution is decreased and mass markers become less reliable. However, many of these errors were eliminated because of the correlative nature of this study, and in doubtful cases, the peak was put in the "unclassified" section. The author welcomes correspondence on any errors which are found by readers, and hopes that such helpful criticism, as well as the increased availability of high resolution spectra — e.g., *(3)* — will largely eliminate such errors in later editions of this table.

Empirical Formula. Only the ion of *m/e* of the most abundant combination of isotopes is classified. If there are multiple possibilities because of the presence of natural or artificial isotopes, the remainder are classified under P.I.D. Thus in a particular spectrum if the $C_{21}H_{15}^+$ ion is the most abundant, the $C_{20}C^{13}H_{15}^+$ ion could well be the fifth most abundant. It is not classified, as its significance is usually fairly obvious from the presence of the larger $C_{21}H_{15}$ peak. In the case of elements with more highly abundant natural isotopes, however, this leads to some possibly unexpected classifications. Thus, the most abundant $CHBr_2^+$ ion is not that containing two atoms of the most abundant of the isotopes, Br^{79}. Because the Br^{81} abundance is nearly that of the Br^{79}, $CHBr_2^+$ gives ions of *m/e* 171, 173, and 175 in a ratio of 1:2:1. Thus, a spectrum giving rise to the $CHBr_2^+$ ion would be referenced only under $CHBr^{79}Br^{81}$, *m/e* 173, and the corresponding isotopic ions at *m/e* 171 and 175 would be tabulated under P.I.D. This should cause no difficulty in the identification of $CHBr_2^+$ from an unknown spectrum, as the largest peak should be used first to identify the ion.

Structural Significance. Where possible, the types of ions causing the empirical formula shown are postulated, and the abundant compound types found are tabulated separately. The justifications for many such structural classifications are due to careful correlations of spectra that have been published by a variety of authors. No attempt has been made to give proper credit or reference to this vital previous work. Such an attempt would seriously complicate the table, and it was also impossible to give proper credit in every case. The author found most helpful a number of unpublished correlations which had been prepared informally by coworkers in the Dow laboratories. In addition, a sizable number of interesting structure-spectral relations were found which are reported for the first time in this table. The theoretical implications of these new correlations will be discussed in separate publications.

The author has had the temerity to make structural classifications and postulate correlations in many cases without rigorous proof. This is partially based on experience and intuition, but it is presumed that a number of such postulations will in time be shown to be incorrect. It is hoped that in most cases these will serve a useful purpose, even if only to stimulate the reader to point out such errors. Where the assignment is in considerable doubt, a question mark has been inserted and, of course, the most dubious cases have been listed under Unclassified.

If there appear to be two ways in which the particular ion in the spectrum could have arisen, it is usually classified under the most probable. If this is uncertain or if it is felt the ion would be considerably less abundant if only one such structural influence were active, it is listed as Unclassified. However, at most mass numbers there are few cases of this. At *m/e* 57 a further breakdown of overlapping mechanisms was attempted because of the very large number of $C_4H_9^+$ ions found. Thus, a second number is listed following that indicating the number of tabulations under the most abundant, etc., peaks to indicate those compounds in which a second structural feature influenced the formation of this peak. For example, in *tert*-butyl ethers the high abundance of the $C_4H_9^+$ ion is caused by the ready cleavage both at the branched *tert*-butyl group and at the alpha bond of the ether.

A homologous series of compounds will be expected to show similarities in structural correlations. Thus, when the classifications for a particular empirical formula were found to be parallel to a lower member of the homologous series, reference has often been made to this lower ion instead of making a complete listing of the possibilities. Since the higher member of the series is usually not represented by as many compound examples in the mass spectral file, it may be that one or more of the structural types indicated for the lower member were not actually found at the higher mass. At *m/e* 200 and above, individual compounds are often listed with the inference that by checking lower members of the homologous series analogous possible structures will be indicated. For the individual compound the postulated mechanism of formation of the particular ion is usually indicated, followed by "etc." where it is thought that the other classifications found for lower members of the homologous series will apply here also. For example, at *m/e* 223, the structure "$Cl(H_7C_3)_2PhCH(CH_3)$-, etc." is listed. Indications of other possible structures can thus be found at *m/e* 189 (which refers to *m/e* 133) and *m/e* 209 (which refers to *m/e* 125) which list molecules in which Cl- and CH_3-, respectively, are replaced by H-. Thus through these cross references one can infer that at *m/e* 223 such structures as $Cl(H_{11}C_5)PhC(CH_3)_2$- and $Cl(CH_3)_2(C_2H_5)_2PhCH(CH_3)$- are also probable.

A number of ion types are placed under P.I.D. (*P*arent, *I*sotopic, *D*oubly charged) instead of being classified separately. It is felt that the parent (molecular) ion is not representative of a structural type, but only of a single compound or group of isomeric compounds. Thus, the usefulness of the molecular ion for structure determination lies more in the indication of empirical formula for the parent molecule and in indicating the structural groups of the molecule through the difference in mass between the parent ion and other prominent peaks in the mass spectrum. The peak at highest *m/e* represents the molecule ion when the molecular has sufficient chemical stability - e.g., unsaturated or cyclic structures. As a further check, the parent will be an "odd-electron" ion with an *m/e* of even number unless the ion contains an odd number of nitrogen atoms *(2, 8)*.

An ion containing a less abundant combination of isotopes, also included under P.I.D., is not classified separately because identification is usually more simple from the more abundant isotopic combination. The mass number and relative abundance of isotopic ions can be calculated from the accompanying table. It might be argued that classification of these could be useful where the more abundant isotopic combination is obscured by another ion of nominally identical mass. This, however, will be an unusual circumstance and can be overcome by careful use of the table or by the use of exact empirical structure determination through high resolution techniques.

Multiply charged ions, a third classification under P.I.D., are rarely of sufficient abundance to be included. Those that were found usually offered little apparent structural significance in addition to the corresponding singly charged ion and were much less abundant, although further work in this field may show helpful correlations. The most common doubly charged ions of sufficient abundance were

NATURAL ABUNDANCES OF COMMON ISOTOPES

Element	Isotope and Natural Abundance (Most Abundant = 100%)
Hydrogen	*1*, 100%; *2*, 0.0156%
Boron	*10*, 23.2% [25.0%, (12)]; *11*, 100%
Carbon	*12*, 100%; *13*, 1.120%
Nitrogen	*14*, 100%; *15*, 0.36%
Oxygen	*16*, 100%; *17*, 0.04%; *18*, 0.20%
Fluorine	*19*, 100%
Silicon	*28*, 100%; *29*, 5.07%; *30*, 3.31%
Phosphorus	*31*, 100%
Sulfur	*32*, 100%; *33*, 0.78%; *34*, 4.39%
Chlorine	*35*, 100%; *37*, 32.7%
Gallium	*69*, 100%; *71*, 66.7%
Germanium	*70*, 56.0%; *72*, 75.0%; *73*, 21.2%; *74*, 100%; *76*, 21.3%
Arsenic	*75*, 100%
Selenium	*74*, 1.92%; *76*, 18.2%; *77*, 15.0%; *78*, 47.4% *80*, 100%; *82*, 17.7%
Bromine	*79*, 100%; *81*, 97.5%
Tin	*112*, 3.07%; *114*, 2.08%; *115*, 1.07%; *116*, 43.6%; *117*, 23.4%; *118*, 72.8%; *119*, 26.5%; *120*, 100%; *122*, 14.5%; *124*, 18.3%
Antimony	*121*, 100%; *123*, 74.7%
Iodine	*127*, 100%
Mercury	*196*, 0.54%; *198*, 33.6%; *199*, 56.9%; *200*, 77.7%; *201*, 44.5%; *202*, 100%; *204*, 23.0%
Lead	*204*, 2.66%; *206*, 50.9%; *207*, 40.4%; *208*, 100%

Most instruments show some mass discrimination which tends to lower the observed abundance of the heavier isotope a few per cent.

found in the spectra of fused ring aromatic hydrocarbons and generally arose from loss of one or more hydrogens from the parent ion. No metastable ions were found of significant abundance, but most of the spectra from the author's laboratory were recorded using a metastable suppressor to eliminate such ions.

No attempt has been made to give the true structure of the ion, if it is actually other than that indicated by the nominal bond cleavages. For example, Meyerson and his coworkers *(12)* have shown that cleavage of the benzylic bond in aromatic hydrocarbons does not give the benzyl ion, $C_6H_5CH_2^+$, but the rearranged tropylium ion. Thus, the entry $PhCH_2 \nmid R$ under *m/e* 91 indicates only the benzylic bond cleavage and not the rearrangement.

Relative Probability of Ions. The final columns of the tabulation, headed 1, 2, 3, and possibly up through 10, show the number of compounds giving peaks of each relative magnitude under each structural classification. Thus, of the 212 compounds studied in which *m/e* 91 is one of the three highest peaks in the spectrum, 48 were found to be formed as the most abundant through the benzylic cleavage loss of an alkoxyl, alkyl, halogen, carbonyl, etc., group. Further, such a cleavage was found to produce the second and third highest peaks in the spectra of 18 and five compounds, respectively. Thus, one can draw the inference in attempting to identify a base (highest) *m/e* 91 peak in an unknown spectrum that one should first check for the possibility of the benzylic structure in the molecule. By similar reasoning a $C_7H_7^+$ ion having a reduced intensity in an unknown spectrum would probably not arise from the $C_6H_5CH_2$- group, but from a more complex structure through a more drastic cleavage or rearrangement.

The usefulness of this probability concept is admittedly in doubt, because the 4000 spectra cataloged, although a large number on the basis of known collections of mass spectra, are still only a small percentage of the total number of organic compounds in the literature.

The distribution of structural types naturally depends somewhat on the interests of the originating laboratory and company. Thus, the large number of $C_6H_3OCl_3^+$ ions tabulated at *m/e* 196 resulted from the study of a sizable group of trichlorophenoxy ester derivatives. However, the compounds of this file generally represent a broad range of chemistry, and a real attempt has been made to include also all classes of compounds whose spectra have been reported in the literature — e.g., steroids and hydrocarbons of high molecular weight. In general, the statistical data are probably meaningful for the "simpler" organic compounds, but of little value for more complex or specialized classes of organic compounds, such as plant pigments, perfluoroaromatic compounds, sugars, etc. Thus, the distribution of relative abundances should be given weight in structure indications generally only where quite a number of compounds of that type were available. For example, as cited above, the data for $C_7H_7^+$ ions indicate that structures containing the benzyl ion have a high probability of giving this *m/e* as the highest peak in the spectrum. However, the absence of a large number of entries for $C_7H_7S^+$ at *m/e* 123 does not indicate that the corresponding thiobenzyl($HSC_6H_4CH_2$-) compounds could not give a very abundant *m/e* 123 peak.

When several structural types are listed for the same formula on one line, they are generally in decreasing order of importance.

SYMBOLS

∤ indicates that this bond is cleaved to form the ion. The group or groups lost, if indicated, are usually designated by general symbols such as R (alkyl) or Y (functional group).

Ph ∤ R ∤ H indicates the loss of the R group with rearrangement of one of its hydrogens to the resulting ion (here $Ph\text{-}H^+$). This should be followed by "(rearr.)." The β-hydrogen atom is usually the one rearranged *(7)*, so that the lack of a β-hydrogen in the compound should greatly reduce the probability of the rearrangement. A double cleavage such as CH_3COO ∤ R ⫲ H_2 indicates the rearrangement of two hydrogen atoms, although in this case the second hydrogen atom need not come from the carbon atom *beta* to the bond cleaved *(10)*.

⫲ indicates two bonds are cleaved (usually *not* the cleavage of a double bond).

RC (R')(R'') ∤ indicates that the bond broken is to the carbon atom and not to R' or R''.

(ABC) ∤ Y means that Y might be substituted on A, B, or C.

"Base" means the highest peak in the spectrum — i.e., the most abundant ion.

A semicolon signifies that the classifications following it are significantly less abundant than the preceding ones. Above *m/e* 218 in the table the semicolon means that the classifications following it were only found as less intense than the fifth most abundant peak.

ΣR indicates a summation of the alkyl groups — i.e., if $R = CH_3$, $R' = C_2H_5$, and $R'' = H$, then $\Sigma R = C_3H_9$.

(C_6F_8). Parentheses around a formula indicate a significant ion (especially for exact mass determination) which was not in the card file, and is therefore not included in the numerical tabulation.

ABBREVIATIONS

aliph.	aliphatic
arom.	aromatic
cleav.	cleavage
corresp.	corresponding
cpd.	compound
dvts.	derivatives
esp.	especially
gp.	group
h. c.	hydrocarbon
mult.	multiple
Ph	phenyl group
P. I. D. Ions	parent, isotopic, or doubly charged ions
R	hydrocarbon moiety (generally aliphatic, but can be a hydrogen atom)
R*	hydrocarbon moiety containing an electronegative group as X, $-NO_2$, -CN, -COOR, -COR, etc. (see Y* below)

rearr. rearrangement (usually of a H atom. If none is indicated, the location of the rearranged H atom is not definite).

satd. saturated

substd. substituted

unsatd. unsaturated

X any halogen atom

Y a functional group

Y_n one or more Y groups

Y* an electronegative functional group, as X, $-NO_2$, -CN, -COOR, -COR, $-SO_2X$, -C≡CH, R*, -NCS, -COX, etc.

Z another functional group or combination of several Y groups.

CONCLUSIONS

Despite the fact that this file cannot possibly contain a representative number of all possible types of organic molecules, the prevalence of certain entries is of interest. A total of 15,746 peaks from the spectra of 4036 compounds were examined, and an assignment of structure and mechanism was attempted for each of these. The most entries are found at *m/e* 43, 41, 57, and 55, representing 5.8, 5.5, 3.5, and 2.6%, respectively, of the total entries for the three most abundant ions. Similarly, the most abundant empirical formulas found were $C_3H_5^+$, $C_3H_7^+$, $C_4H_9^+$, $C_4H_7^+$, $C_2H_3O^+$, and $C_7H_7^+$, representing 5.3, 4.0, 3.0, 2.4, 1.5, and 1.5%, respectively, of the total number of entries for the three most abundant ions. Figures A, B, and C represent the number of entries which were found for the first, second, and third most abundant ions, respectively, at each nominal mass number.

The number of peaks to which no appreciable structural significance could be assigned ("other unclassified") was gratifyingly low. Separation between peaks classified as P.I.D. and "other unclassified" ions was not made for all *m/e* below *m/e* 103, but these types together represented only 11% of the total, so that the "unclassified" alone should be under 5%. At the higher mass numbers the "other unclassified" ions were 9% of the total. The fact that such a high percentage of the major ions in this wide variety of mass spectra are explainable indicates the potential of the method for molecular structure determination, and the significant progress that has been made within the last decade on the fundamentals of ion decomposition paths.

Space has been left in the table, especially at the higher *m/e*, for the addition of correlations found subsequently by the reader. This, of course, will increase the usefulness of the tabulation in the areas of the reader's particular chemical interests. The author would appreciate it if any such additional correlations could be forwarded for inclusion in a possible future edition of the table. To reiterate, it would be very helpful to hear of alternative explanations of mechanisms for the data shown or of any errors found.

Often the neutral fragment lost is of as much structural significance as the ion formed. Thus it should be possible to construct a similar tabulation using the mass of the difference between the abundant ion

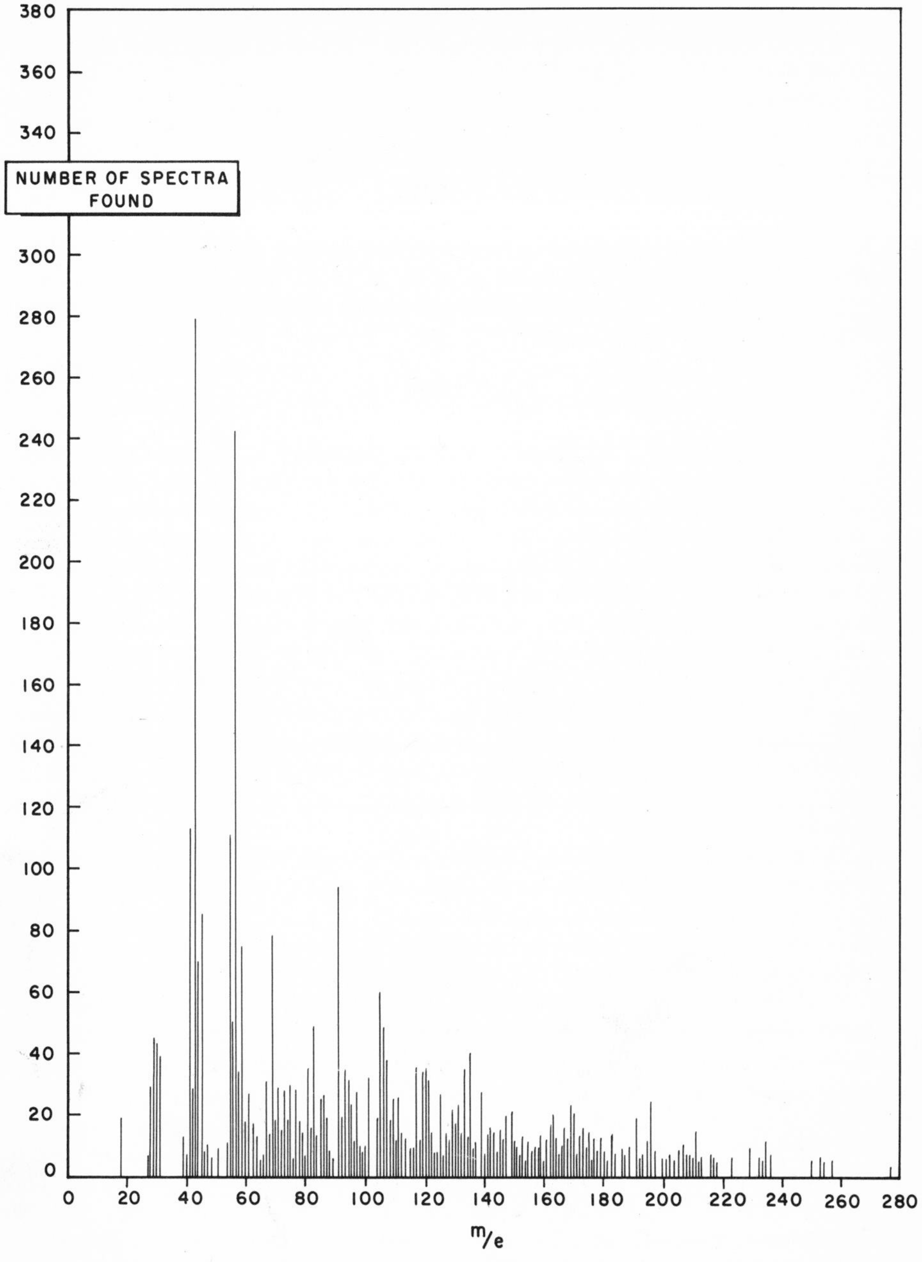

Figure 1. Number of spectra in which ions of a particular m/e were the most abundant

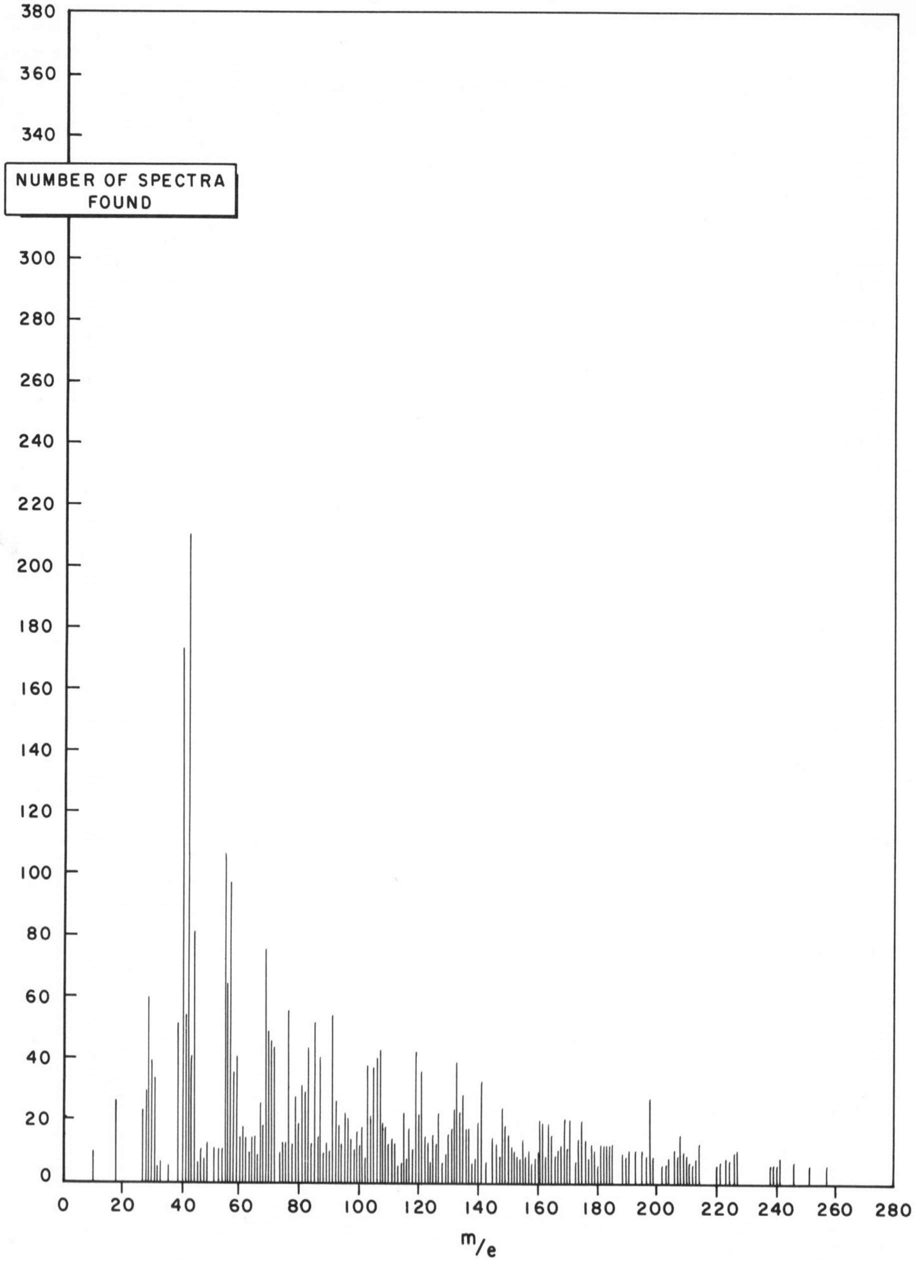

Figure 2. Number of spectra in which ions of a particular m/e were second most abundant

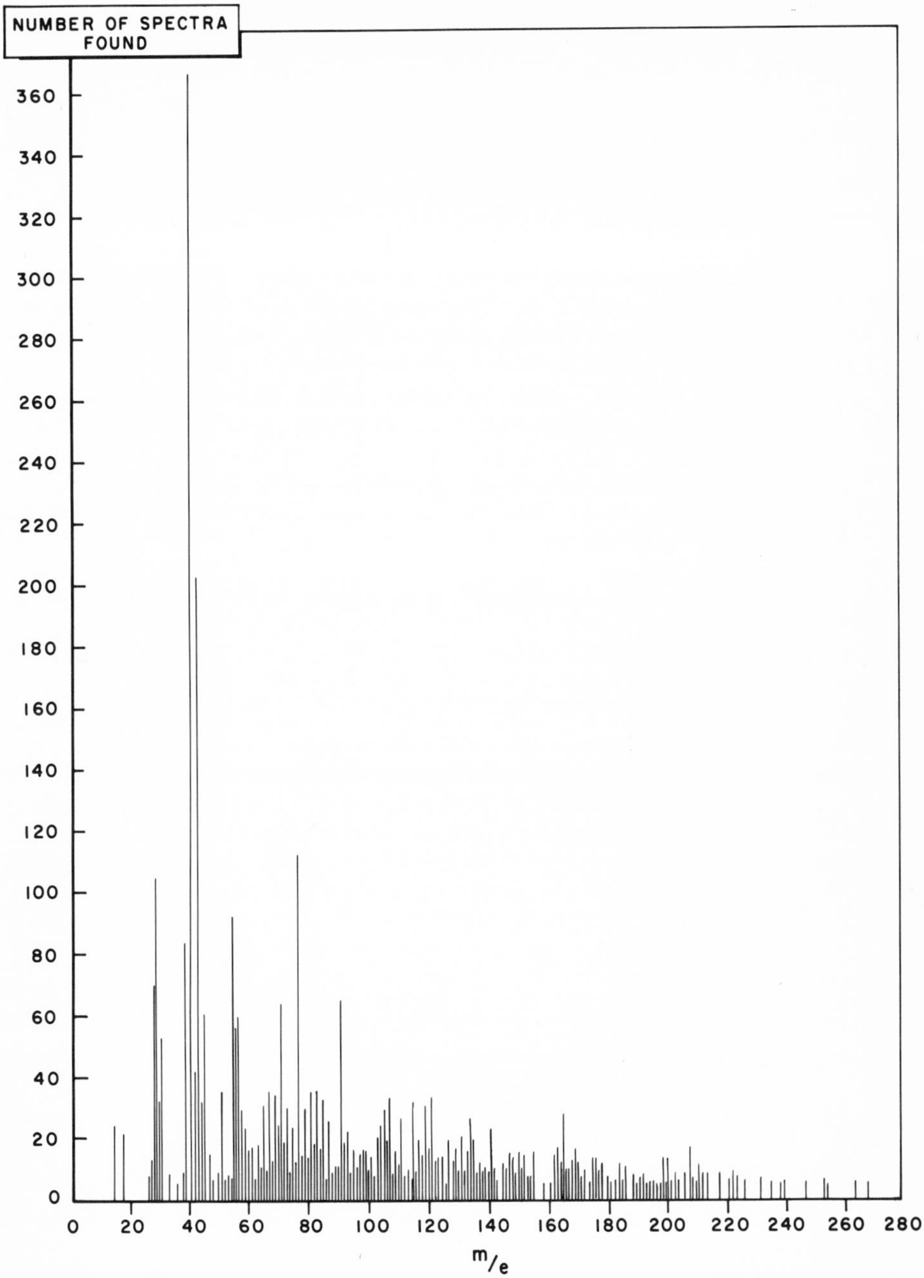

Figure 3. Number of spectra in which ions of a particular m/e were third most abundant

found and the molecular ion. With such a table, functional groups which ordinarily do not retain the positive charge on cleavage of the molecular ion, such as the methyl group, halogen atoms, etc., could be classified and more easily identified. Such correlations fail, of course, when the abundant ion is formed from a fragment ion instead of the molecular ion, but the incidence of such cases would be of interest. Preparing such tabulations with the file cards used in the present study should be simplified because degradation paths have already been assigned. However, the preparation of such a correlation should await an assessment of the usefulness of the present tabulation.

In the past few years, the markedly increased use of mass spectrometry in the solution of complex problems in molecular structure has been most gratifying. It is hoped that this tabulation will encourage this use by directly aiding both the neophyte and expert in structure identification. Possibly of greater importance, however, is the demonstration of the high percentage of the abundant ions in mass spectra to which meaningful structure assignments can be made, demonstrating the maturity of the method and the unique usefulness of its molecular structure information.

ACKNOWLEDGMENT

This paper embodies efforts and ideas of such a large number of personnel of the Mass Spectrometry Section of the Chemical Physics Research Laboratory of The Dow Chemical Co. That it should be called the "Dow Table" of prominent ions in mass spectra. The structure and principles of this table evolved from invaluable discussions with R. S. Gohlke over a period of several years. Among others whose contributions are gratefully acknowledged are Jo Ann Gilpin, Joanne M. Rupprecht, Marjorie A. Eash, William T. Shelburg, and Eugene O. Camehl. The author is also happy to thank Norman Wright and Victor J. Caldecourt for inspiration and counsel, Priscilla A. Turner for stenographic assistance, and Charlotte M. Cripps for tabulations.

LITERATURE CITED

(1) Beynon, J. H., "Advances in Mass Spectrometry," p. 328, Pergamon Press, London, 1959.

(2) Beynon, J. H., "Mass Spectrometry and Its Applications to Organic Chemistry," Elsevier, Amsterdam, 1960.

(3) Beynon, J. H., Saunders, R. A., Williams, A. E., *Anal. Chem.*, 33, 221 (1961).

(4) Colthup, N. B., *J. Opt. Soc. Am.*, 40, 397 (1950).

(5) Doederer, G. C., Olsen, R. S., *Appl. Spectroscopy,* 16, 25 (1962).

(6) Kuentzel, L. E., *Anal. Chem.*, 23, 1413 (1951).

(7) McLafferty, F. W., *Ibid.*, 31, 82 (1959).

(8) McLafferty, F. W., "Mass Spectrometry," in "Determination of Organic Structures by Physical Methods," F. C. Nachod and W. D. Phillips, eds., Academic Press, New York, 1962.

(9) McLafferty, F. W., Gohlke, R. S., *Anal. Chem.*, 31, 1160 (1959).

(10) McLafferty, F. W., Hamming, M. C., *Chem. and Ind. (London)* 1958, 1366.

(11) Mass Spectral Data File, Committee E-14, American Society for Testing Materials, 1916 Race St., Philadelphia, Pa.

(12) Rylander, P. N., Meyerson, Seymour, Grubb, Henry, *J. Am. Chem. Soc.*, 79, 8482 (1957).

(13) Shapiro, I., Ditter, J. F., *J. Chem. Phys.*, 26, 798 (1957).

(14) Von Hoehne, J., Users' Clinic, Consolidated Electrodynamics Corp., New Orleans, June 1958.

(15) Zemany, P. D., *Anal. Chem.*, 22, 920 (1950).

Correlations of Mass Spectral Data

m/e	Formula	Structural Significance*	1†	2	3	4	5	6	Total
1.0078	H			1				1	2
2.0156	H_2	P.I.D.-2					1	1	4
3.									0
4.		P.I.D.-1							1
5.									0
6.									0
7.									0
8.									0
9.									0
10.									0
11.0093	B							1	1
12.0000	C	Small molecules		2	1	4	4	5	16
13.0018	CH	Small molecules				2	3		5

(Columns 1†–6: Relative Probability)

* For meaning of symbols, see page 7 of text; for abbrevations, see page 7.

† Number of spectra in which the most abundant ion has this *m/e*.

m/e	Formula	Structural Significance	Relative Probability 1	2	3	4	5	6	7	Total
14.0031	N			2	1	1	2	3		9
14.0156	CH_2			1	1	3	3	7		15
		Unclassified				1		2		3
		Total		3	2	5	5	12		27
15.0235	CH_3	Hydrocarbons		1						1
		R-|-Y (Y=-COOR)		1	3	1				5
		(Y=-COR)		5	6	2				13
		(Y=-OR)			4	10				14
		(Y=-NR_2)		1		4				5
		(Y= X, -NO_2)	1		2	2				5
		(Y=-HgR, -N=NR)	2							2
		(Y=-OCOR*)	1		5	4				10
		Other compounds		1	2	5				8
		P.I.D. and unclassified			2	1				3
		Total	4	9	24	29				66
15.9949	O			1	3	1	3			8
16.0187	H_2N			1		3	3			7
		P.I.D. and unclassified	1				1			2
		Total	1	2	3	4	7			17
17.0027	HO		1	1	2		1			5
17.0265	H_3N		1	3		4				8
		P.I.D. and unclassified	1			1				2
		Total	3	4	2	5	1			15
18.0106	H_2O	(Data not meaningful, as no rigorous effort to remove H_2O from most samples. H_2O also from hydrates, thermal decomp.)	19	26	21					66
18.0344	H_4N	Total	19	26	21					66
18.9984	F							1	1	2
19.0184	H_3O						2		3	5
		P.I.D. and unclassified		1		1				2
		Total		1		1	2	1	4	9
20.		P.I.D. and unclassified	1	1			1	2		5
21.		P.I.D. and unclassified			1					1
22.		P.I.D. and unclassified		1		1				2

m/e	Formula	Structural Significance	1	2	3	4	5	6	7	Total
23.0264	B_2H						1			1
24.0000	C_2	Highly unsatd. h.c.			2			1	1	4
24.0343	B_2H_2				1					1
		Total			3		1	1	1	5
25.0078	C_2H	Highly unsatd. h.c.		1	2	2				5
25.0421	B_2H_3					1				1
		P.I.D. and unclassified			1					1
		Total		1	3	3				7
26.0031	CN	R ‡ CN, $RCHN_2$		2	5	1				8
26.0156	C_2H_2			1	2	6				9
26.0499	B_2H_4		1							1
		P.I.D. and unclassified	1			2				3
		Total	2	3	7	9				21
27.0235	C_2H_3	CH_2=CH ‡ R		2						2
		Other h.c.		2	5					7
		CH_2=CH ‡ COR, CH_2=CH ‡ COOR	1	5						6
		CH_2=CH ‡ X, CH_2=CH ‡ COOR	1	2						3
		X ‡ CH_2CH ‡ HY (Y= -COOR', X, etc.)	2	8						10
		Other compounds	1	16	2					19
27.0406	CH_4B	CH_3BH-, higher boron alkyls		3	5					8
27.0577	B_2H_5			2						2
		P.I.D. and unclassified	2	3	1					6
		Total	7	43	13					63
27.9949	CO	Lactones (could be C_2H_4)		4	2					6
		Other (also possible from action of O_2 on electron filament)		1	2					3
28.0061	N_2	(N_2 gas impurity is possible, although eliminated where recognizable)								
28.0187	CH_2N (or C_2H_4)	Ethylenimines	2	1						3
		Alkyl amines, esp. $(CH_3)_2N$-	2	8	20					30
28.0313	C_2H_4	Satd. h.c.	2	1						3
		Dialkylaromatic h.c.		3	1					4
		Other compounds		2	5					7
		Unclassified (C_2H_4, CO, or CH_2N	20	20	33					73
		P.I.D. and unclassified	3	3	6					12
		Total	29	43	69					141

Relative Probability: columns 1–7.

m/e	Formula	Structural Significance	Relative Probability 1	2	3	Total
29.0027	CHO	R+CHO (R < C_5)	4	2	2	8
		RO+CHO		4	2	6
		Epoxides		1	3	4
		Mixed ROR, ROH	1	8	23	32
29.0391	C_2H_5	C_2H_5+Y (Y= -CHRR', -CRR'R'')		1	5	6
		(Y= -CH_2PhR)		1	2	3
		(Y= -COOR)	1	10	5	16
		(Y= -$CONR_2$)			1	1
		(Y= -COR)	1	4	4	9
		(Y= -SR or -SSR)	3	2	1	6
		(Y= -OR)	5	2	5	12
		(Y= -OCOR*)	15	5	3	23
		(Y= X)		2	1	3
		(Y= -ONO, -CX_3, -ONO_2, -HgR, -CNS, -NO_2, etc.)	5	2	3	10
		Satd. h. c.	1	1	2	4
		Cpds. with satd. h. c. moieties	7	5	32	44
		P. I. D. and unclassified	2	9	10	21
		Total	45	59	104	208
29.9826	H_2Si	H_2Si+R_2	1			1
29.9980	NO	Aliph. and arom. nitro cpds.		4	3	7
		R_2N+NO (nitrosamines)	1	1	2	4
		RONO, $RONO_2$, etc.	2	1	1	4
30.0344	CH_4N	R+CH_2NH_2	26	7	2	35
		R+CH_2NH+R'+H (rearr.)	3	10	6	19
		Combination of above		5	1	6
		R+CH_2N+(R'+H)$_2$ (rearr.)		5	5	10
		RCH(CH_3)NH_2 cpds. (*m/e* 44 is base peak)		2	3	5
		RCO+$NHCH_2$+R' (rearr.)	4	2	2	8
		P. I. D. and unclassified	6	2	7	15
		Total	43	39	32	114
30.9984	CF			4	17	21
31.0184	CH_3O	R+CH_2OH (many of these cpds. have other possible sources of *m/e* 31)	18	14	16	48
		R+CH_2O+R'+H (rearr.) (mainly ethoxides; dioxanes, etc.)	6	6	5	17
		Y-$\overset{O}{\overset{\|}{M}}$+$OCH_2$+R' (rearr.) (M= C, S, P, As; Y= RO-, RNH-, RCO-, R-Ph-, etc.)	3	6		9
		HCO+OCH_2+R (rearr.) (formates)	5		1	6
		CH_3O+OR, CH_3O+$CONH_2$		2		2
		Cpds. having more abundant $C_nH_{2n+1}O$ peak (mainly *m/e* 59)		4	17	21
		P. I. D. and unclassified	7	4	9	20
		Total	39	43	53	135

m/e	Formula	Structural Significance	1	2	3	4	5	6	Total
31.9721	S			3	1	2	1		7
31.9898	O_2	(O_2 gas impurity common, removed where recognized)							
32.0262	CH_4O				1	2			3
	Also:	CHF, CH_6N(?), PH				5	4		9
		P.I.D. and unclassified	4	2					6
		Total	4	5	2	9	5		25
33.0140	CH_2F	R†CH_2F	1	2	6			3	12
		Other (rearr.)		1		4		1	6
33.0340	CH_5O	$HOCH_2$†CH_2OR‡H_2 (rearr.), $HOCH_2$† CHRR'‡H_2 (rearr.)?		2	1	1		1	5
	Also:	H_2P (PH_3), HS (H_2S)		1	1				2
		P.I.D. and unclassified	1			2			3
		Total	2	6	8	7		5	28
33.9877	H_2S	R†CS-NH_2 (R = aromatic); C_2H_5SH			1	1		1	3
		P.I.D. and unclassified	2	1	1	1	1		6
		Total	2	1	2	2	1	1	9
34.9689	Cl	Small molecule, Cl mainly on -CO-, S, P, -CN, -CX_2-, etc.		1	3		2	4	10
34.9955	H_3S	CH_3SCH_3					1		1
		P.I.D. and unclassified		1	1	1	1	1	5
		Total		2	4	1	4	5	16
35.9767	HCl	Cpds. with "active" Cl (and chlorides, etc.). May be HCl from thermal decomp.	4	5	4	7			20
		P.I.D. and unclassified			1	2			3
		Total	4	5	5	9			23
37.0078	C_3H	Highly unsatd. or halogenated small molecules (h. c., furans, etc.)				2	5	7	14
		P.I.D. and unclassified	1		1	2			4
		Total	1		1	4	5	7	18

m/e	Formula	Structural Significance	Relative Probability 1	2	3	4	5	Total
38.0031	C_2N	RR'C=CR"-CN		1	1	1		
38.0156	C_3H_2	Highly unsatd., halogenated, etc. small molecules (h.c., furans, etc.)		2	4	6		12
		P.I.D. and unclassified		1	3	3		7
		Total		4	8	10		22
39.0109	C_2HN	C_3H_5CN (C_3H_3?)			3			3
39.0235	C_3H_3	HC≡C-CH_2 ǂ Y (Y = X, -H)	3	1				4
		Dienes	2	5	6			13
		Cyclic olefins, acetylenic h.c.		5	10			15
		Olefins		1	11			12
		H_2 ǂ C_3H_3 ǂ COR	6	1	8			15
		C_3H_5Y, $C_3H_4Y_2$, RC_3H_4Y (Y = X, O, S)		14	10			24
		Furans	2	2	8			12
		Other heterocyclics (pyridines (C_2HN?), etc.)		1	15			16
		Aromatics (mainly di- to tetra-subst.)			8			8
		Others		1	4			5
		Total	13	31	83			127
40.0187	C_2H_2N	R ǂ CH_2CN, R ǂ CH=CH-N ǂ R' (cyclic), etc.		1	3	5	1	10
40.0313	C_3H_4	Dienes, acetylenes, cyclic olefins, etc.	2	2		4	8	16
		RC_3H_4Y (Y= -Cl, -COR, S; R= H, -CH_3)			1	1	3	5
	Also:	OCBH, C_2O (C_3O_2)	2					2
		P.I.D. and unclassified	3			1	1	5
		Total	7	3	4	11	13	38
41.0027	C_2HO				1			1
41.0265	C_2H_3N	Nitriles, RCN	4	3	4			11
		Pyrroles		2				2
41.0391	C_3H_5	Cyclopropyl ǂ Y (Y=R, -COR)	1	4	1			6
		CH_2=CH-CH_2 ǂ R	12	5	2			19
		CH_2 = C(CH_3) ǂ R	3	3	1			7
		CH_3-CH=CH ǂ R	3	2	9			14
		Other h.c.	27	38	95			160
		Cpds. with h.c. moieties	24	105	237			366

m/e	Formula	Structural Significance	Relative Probability 1	2	3	Total
		C_3H_5 ╪ Y (Y= -COR; -CN)	10	9	7	26
		(Y= -OR, -SR, $-NR_2$)	11	1	3	15
		(Y= -OCOR*, -NRCOR*)	3	1	4	8
		(Y= X)	5			5
41.0562	C_2H_6B	$(CH_3)_2B$-, higher boranes	13			13
		P.I.D. and unclassified	1		2	3
		Total	117	173	366	656
42.0106	C_2H_2O	H ╪ CH_2CO ╪ Br	1			1
42.0343	C_2H_4N	Ethylenimines, $CH_3CH=N$ ╪	3	1		4
42.0469	C_3H_6	$CH_2=CHCH_2$ ╪ R ╪ H; cyclopropyl ╪ R ╪ H (rearrs.)	2	5	1	8
		Other h. c.	1	4	5	10
		Other compounds	3	5	1	9
	C_3H_6, C_2H_2O, or C_2H_4N	Unclassified	17	19	34	70
		P.I.D. and other unclassified	2			2
		Total	29	24	41	104
43.0058	CHNO	R-O ╪ CONH ╪ H, R_2N ╪ CONH ╪ H(?)	4		1	5
43.0184	C_2H_3O	CH_3CO ╪ R	30	4	14	48
		CH_3CO ╪ OR	36	7	11	54
		CH_3CO ╪ NR_2	2	5	17	24
		Cyclic ethers	4	11	4	19
		Other satd. ROH, ROR, mixed	5	7	15	27
		$CH_2=CHO$ ╪ R		2	3	5
		Other		1	2	3
43.0296	CH_3N_2	$CH_3N=N$ ╪ CH_3		1		1
43.0421	C_2H_5N	Cyclic amines	2			2
		Other	3			3
43.0547	C_3H_7	$(CH_3)_2CH$ ╪ C_nH_{2n+1}	29	8		37
		Other $(CH_3)_2CH$ ╪ R, $(CH_3)_2CH$ ╪ RY	31	20	20	71
		$CH_3CH_2CH_2$ ╪ CHRR', ╪ CRR'R" (branched)	9	3	1	13
		$CH_3CH_2CH_2$ ╪ R (R= -C-C=C, -C-Ph)	2	1	1	4
		Other $CH_3CH_2CH_2$ ╪ C_nH_{2n+1}	43	33	20	96
		Cpds. with large satd. h.c. groups	26	82	80	188

m/e	Formula	Structural Significance	Relative Probability 1	2	3	Total
43.0547	C_3H_7 (Cont'd.)					
		C_3H_7— Y (Y= -COOR)	9	4		13
		(Y= -$CONR_2$)		1	1	2
		(Y= -COR)	5	1		6
		(Y= -NR_2)			1	1
		(Y= -SR or -SSR)	4		4	8
		(Y= -OR)	10	4	2	16
		(Y= -OCOR*)	4	5	3	12
		(Y= X)	5			5
		(Y= -NO_2)	2			2
		P.I.D. and unclassified	13	9	5	27
		Total	279	210	203	692
43.9898	CO_2	Decomposition, as CO_3^{-2} salts	2		2	4
		R* ‡ COO ‡ H (or ‡ R')?	3	4	4	11
44.0136	CH_2NO	H_2NCO ‡ R, H_2NCO ‡ OR	8	7	1	16
44.0262	C_2H_4O	OCH-CH_2 ‡ R ‡ H (rearr.)	4	2	1	7
		CH_2=CHO ‡ R ‡ H (rearr.)	1	1	1	3
		Oxiranes, dioxalanes	2	3		5
		Other		6	2	8
44.0499	C_2H_6N	$H_2NCH(CH_3)$ ‡ R	10	1		11
		R ‡ $CH(CH_3)NH$ ‡ R' ‡ H (rearr.)	3	1		4
		CH_3NHCH_2 ‡ R	5			5
		R ‡ $CH_2N(CH_3)$ ‡ R' ‡ H (rearr.)	1	3	4	8
		$(CH_3)_2N$ ‡ CR_2Ph	17	1		18
		$(CH_3)_2N$ ‡ COR	2	1		3
		Cpds. having a more abundant $C_nH_{2n+1}N$ peak		7	9	16
		Other	6		1	7
		P.I.D. and unclassified	6	3	6	15
		Total	70	40	31	141
44.9799	CHS	Thiacycloalkane or R-S-R'Y	1	4	10	15
		Thiophene dvts.			11	11
44.9976	CHO_2	HOOC ‡ R*	2	7	3	12
45.0060	CH_5Si	CH_3SiH_2 - ? (by rearr.)		1	1	2
45.0140	C_2H_2F	C_2H_2F ‡ X, C_2H_2F ‡ HX_2	1	5	2	8
45.0340	C_2H_5O	$HOCH_2CH_2$ ‡ Y (Y=-OR, -NR_2,-SR)	10	7	5	22
		$CH_3CH(OH)$ ‡ R	22	10	2	34
		CH_3CH (OH) ‡ COOR, CH_3OCH_2 ‡ COOR	4			4
		CH_3OCH_2 ‡ R	11	2	3	16
		R ‡ CH $(CH_3)O$ ‡ R' ‡ H (rearr.)	9	4	5	18
		R ‡ CH $(CH_3)O$ ‡ COCHY ‡ H (rearr.) (Y= H or R*)	3	3	1	7
		RO ‡ CH_2CH_2O ‡ COR* (rearr.), PhO ‡ CH_2CH_2O ‡ C-CHR* ‡ H (rearr.) etc.	7	4	2	13

m/e	Formula	Structural Significance	Relative Probability 1	2	3	4	5	Total
45.0340	C_2H_5O	(Cont'd.)						
		Cpds. having a more abundant $C_nH_{2n+1}O$ peak		7	6			13
		Others	6	8	5			19
45.0578	C_2H_7N	$(H_3C)_2N$ ∤ CH_2Ph (Y) -OH (rearr.) (*m/e* 44 is larger)		14	3			17
		P.I.D. and unclassified	10	5	1			16
		Total	86	81	60			227
45.9877	CH_2S	Mainly cyclic sulfides	3	1		4		8
45.9929	O_2N	$RONO_2$, CH_3NO_2	3		1			4
46.0296	C_2H_3F			1				1
46.0418	C_2H_6O					1	1	2
		P.I.D. and unclassified	2	4	2	1	1	10
		Total	8	6	3	6	2	25
46.9687	OP	$POCl_3$					1	1
46.9689	CCl				2	2	8	12
46.9853	H_3OSi	$C_4H_9Si(CH_3)_2OH$ (rearr.)				1		1
46.9955	CH_3S	$HSCH_2$ ∤ R	4	4	2	2	4	16
		H_3CS ∤ R	1		2	4	2	9
		R-CH_2S-R' (rearr.) etc.	1	2	6	3	5	17
47.0132	CH_3O_2	R ∤ CH(O ∤ $CH_2CH_3)_2$ (rearr.)? (C_2H_7O?)	1	2		1	2	6
47.0296	C_2H_4F	C_2H_4F ∤ R; $CF_3CHClCF_2CH_2OH$ (rearr.)	3		1	1		5
47.0496	C_2H_7O	CH_3OCH_2 ∤ CHROH, $HOCH_2CHROH$ (mult. rearrs.)		1			2	3
47.0607	H_3B_4	B_4H_3 ∤ H_7, B_4H_3 ∤ BH_8				1	1	2
		P.I.D. and unclassified		1	1	1	1	4
		Total	10	10	14	16	26	76
47.9670	OS	SO_n, SOX_n, etc.		3	1		1	5
47.9767	CHCl		1	1	1		4	7
47.9931	H_4OSi	$PhOSi(CH_3)_3$ (rearr.)		1				1
48.0000	C_4	HC≡CC≡CH				1		1
48.0034	CH_4S	$HSCHRCH_2CHO$, R ∤ SCH_2 ∤ R', $HSCH_2$ ∤ CH_2OH (mult. rearrs.)	1		3	1		5
48.0685	H_4B_4	B_4H_4 ∤ H_6	1					1
		P.I.D. and unclassified		2			1	3
		Total	3	7	5	2	6	23

m/e	Formula	Structural Significance	Relative Probability 1	2	3	4	Total
48.9845	CH_2Cl	$ClCH_2$ + R	5	7	2	7	21
		Cl + $\overset{\ }{C}HCl$ + R + H,					
		Cl_2 + CCl + R ‡ H_2 (rearrs.)		3	1	1	5
49.0061	BF_2	BF_3	1				1
49.0078	C_4H	HC≡CC≡H, HC≡CCH=CH_2		1		1	2
49.0763	H_5B_4	B_4H_5 + H_5		1			1
		P.I.D. and unclassified			1	1	2
		Total	6	12	4	10	32
49.9923	CH_3Cl	CH_2Cl + COO + H,					
		CH_2Cl + CO + H (rearrs.)	2				2
49.9968	CF_2	F_2YCY' (Y or Y' = -X, -CN,					
		$-CX_3$, -COR)		1	4	7	12
50.0031	C_3N	NC-C≡C + H, NC(-C=C-)Y					
		(Y= -X, -CN)		1	1	1	3
50.0156	C_4H_2	Unsatd. alkynes, Ph-Y*			3	10	13
		Pyridine-Y dvts. (Y= H, Y*)					
		(C_3N?)				3	3
50.0841	H_6B_4						
		P.I.D. and unclassified	2				2
		Total	4	2	8	21	35
51.0046	CHF_2	CHF_2 + R	5	2			7
		CXF_2 + R, CF_2=CRY (rearrs.)	1	1	2		4
51.0109	C_3HN	NC-C_2H ‡ HCN	2				2
51.0235	C_4H_3	Alkyne dvts.		3	1		4
		Ph-Y*		1	24		25
		Pyridine-Y* dvts. (C_3HN?)		1	6		7
		P.I.D. and unclassified	1	2	2		5
		Total	9	10	35		54
52.0187	C_3H_2N	NC-CH=CH + R, etc.	2	1	1		4
52.0313	C_4H_4	Alkynes, Ph-Y, pyridine-Y					
		(C_3H_2N?)	1	2	3	1	7
		P.I.D. and unclassified	2	1	2	1	6
		Total	5	4	6	2	17
53.0265	C_3H_3N	NC-C_2H_3 ‡ HCN,					
		NCC_2H_3 ‡ (H)OROH	2	1			3
53.0391	C_4H_5	Alkynes, dienes		5	6		11
		C_4H_5 ‡ HX_2, furans, etc.		4	2		6
		P.I.D. and unclassified	1				1
		Total	3	10	8		21

m/e	Formula	Structural Significance	Relative Probability 1	2	3	Total
53.9980	C_2ON	NC-CO ⫲ CH_3		1		1
54.0106	C_3H_2O	Maleic anhydride	1			1
54.0343	C_3H_4N	$NCCH_2CH_2$ ⫲ Y (Y= -OR, $-CH_2X$, -SR, X, H, -RCN)	4	6	5	15
54.0469	C_4H_6	Alkynes, cyclohexenes, C_4H_6 ⫲ SO_2, H_2N (H) ⫲ C_4H_6 ⫲ (H) CHOH	3	2		5
		P.I.D. and unclassified	3	2	1	6
		Total	11	10	7	28
55.0184	C_3H_3O	H_2C=CHCO ⫲ R	11		4	15
		4-R-cyclohexanones, others, etc.	5		1	6
55.0421	C_3H_5N	Imidazolines	1	1		2
55.0547	C_4H_7	H_2C=CHCH(CH_3) ⫲ R, H_2C=C(C_2H_5) ⫲ R	6	2	3	11
		CH_3CH=CHCH$_2$ ⫲ R, C_2H_5 CH=CH ⫲ R	10	7	7	24
		Other alkenes	7	4	6	17
		Cycloalkanes	26	28	19	73
		Cpds. with h.c. moieties	37	58	48	143
		C_4H_7 ⫲ OR	2	3	1	6
		C_4H_7 ⫲ COR	2	3		5
		C_4H_7 ⫲ HX_2	3	1	2	6
55.0719	C_3H_8B	$C_2H_5B(CH_3)$-	1		1	2
		P.I.D. and unclassified	None			
		Total	111	107	92	310
56.0262	C_3H_4O			3	1	4
56.0500	C_3H_6N		3	1	1	5
56.0626	C_4H_8	CH_3- (C_3H_4) ⫲ R ⫲ H (rearr.) (*m/e* 41 is also large)	3	1		4
		Other olefinic h.c. (*m/e* 41 is also large)	2	3	5	10
		Methylcyclopentyl h.c.	7	2	1	10
		Cyclohexanes, other cycloalkanes	4	2		6
		H ⫲ CH_2C (CH_3)$_2$ ⫲ R (*m/e* 57 usually larger)	1	16	4	21
		H ⫲ C_2H_4CH (CH_3) ⫲ R (*m/e* 57 large)	1	2	1	4
		H ⫲ C_4H_8 ⫲ Y (Y= -OR, -SR)	2	4	2	8
		(Y= -OCOR, -OCOR*)	4	10	8	22
		(Y= X)	2		1	3
		R ⫲ C_4H_8 ⫲ Y (R = C_2H_5, C_3H_7; Y= -SR, -OR, X, -OCOH)	9	2	4	15
		Cyclohexylamine cpds.	4		1	5
		Others	4		1	5
		C_4H_8, C_3H_4O or C_3H_6N unclassified	7	15	22	44
		P.I.D. and other unclassified	1	3	2	6
		Total	50	64	55	169

m/e	Formula	Structural Significance	Relative Probability 1	2	3	Total
57.0340	C_3H_5O	C_2H_5CO ǂ R	4	3		7
		C_2H_5CO ǂ OR	14	2	2	18
		C_2H_5CO ǂ NR_2			1	1
		HOC_3H_4 ǂ R, R ǂ C_3H_4 – O ǂ R' ǂ H (rearr.), C_3H_5O ǂ COR	8	2	2	12
		$\overline{OCH_2C}HCH_2$ ǂ X	2			2
		Mixed ROR, ROH	3	1	4	8
57.0704	C_4H_9	$(CH_3)_3C$ ǂ C_nH_{2n+1}	19+4*	3+0		26
		Other $(CH_3)_3C$ ǂ	12+13	7+1	8+2	43
		$C_2H_5CH(CH_3)$ ǂ C_nH_{2n+1}	4+1	3+2	0+2	12
		Other $C_2H_5CH(CH_3)$ ǂ	2+6	0+4	2+4	18
		Other H_9C_4 ǂ C_nH_{2n+1}	27	32	11	70
		Other cpds. with satd. h.c. moieties	37	9	15	61
		C_4H_9 ǂ Y (Y= -CHRR', -CRR'R")	16+5	8+2	3+2	36
		(Y= -C-C=C)	2	1		3
		(Y= -C-Ph)			1	1
		(Y= -COOR)	1+1		0+1	3
		(Y= $-CONR_2$)	1			1
		(Y= -COR)	1+1	1	1+3	7
		(Y= $-NR_2$)	0+1		1+1	3
		(Y= -SR or -SSR)	0+5		0+1	6
		(Y= -OR)	13+6	2+1	2+1	25
		(Y= -OCOR*)	8	5+1	1	15
		(Y= X)	4+5		0+1	10
		(Y= $-NO_2$, -CNS, $-OSO_2R$, $-BO_3R_2$)	2	1+1	1	5
		Cycloalkyl-OH, $-NH_2$(C_4H_9?)	8	2	2	12
		P.I.D. and unclassified	4	2	4	10
		Total	193+49	84+13	61+17	417
			242	97	78	
58.0293	C_2H_4NO	$HCONHCH_2$ ǂ R, HON=C(CH_3) ǂ R		1	1	2
58.0418	C_3H_6O	CH_3COCH_2 ǂ R ǂ H, H ǂ R ǂ CH_2COCH_2 ǂ R ǂ H, HCOCH (CH_3) ǂ R ǂ H (rearrs.)	1	6	2	9
		Other	3	6	12	21

* Added figure – e.g., +4 – indicates number of compounds in which an additional functional group could be aiding structural feature indicated as causing abundant $C_4H_9^+$ – e.g., $(CH_3)_3C$ ǂ OR.

m/e	Formula	Structural Significance	Relative Probability			
			1	2	3	Total
58.0656	C_3H_8N	$H_2NCH(C_2H_5)$ + R, $H_2NC(CH_3)_2$+R, R + C $(C_2)NH$ + R' + H (rearr.)	3		2	5
		$H_3CNHCH(CH_3)$ + R, R + CH $(CH_3)N(CH_3)$ + R' + H (rearr.)	3			3
		$(CH_3)_2NCH_2$ + R	10			10
		$C_2H_5NCH_2$ + R	2			2
		R + $CH_2N(C_2H_5)$ + R' + H (Rearr.)	5	6	4	15
		RCO + N $(C_2H_5)CH_2$ + R'	2	3		3
		Cpds. having a more abundant $C_nH_{2n+2}N$ peak		5	7	12
		Others	4	2		6
		P.I.D. and unclassified	1	6	1	8
		Total	34	35	29	98
58.9829	CNHS	SCN + C_2H_4 + H (rearr.)		1		1
58.9955	C_2H_3S	Cyclic S cpds.		2	1	3
59.0133	$C_2H_3O_2$	CH_3OCO + R*	7	3	3	13
59.0297	C_3H_4F		2	1	2	5
59.0371	C_2H_5NO	H_2NCOCH_2 + R + H; HON=$CHCH_2$ + R + H (rearrs.)	10			10
59.0496	C_3H_7O	$HOC(CH_3)_2$ + R	13	2	2	17
		$HOCH(C_2H_5)$ + R	5		1	6
		R + $C(CH_3)_2O$ + R' + H, R + $CH(C_2H_5)O$ + R' + H (rearrs.)	3	4		7
		$CH_3OCH(CH_3)$ + R	7			7
		$C_2H_5OCH_2$ + R	5	8	3	16
		$CH_3OCH_2CH_2$ + OR	3	1	1	5
		$HOCH_2CH(CH_3)$ + OR	6	1		7
		$HOCH(CH_3)CH_2$ + OR		1	3	4
		Cpds. having a more abundant $C_nH_{2n+1}O$ peak		3	1	4
		Others	1	3		4
59.0609	$C_2H_7N_2$	$CH_3NHN(CH_3)$-		1	1	2
59.0778	B_5H_4	$B_4B^{10}H_5$, etc.	1		1	2
		P.I.D. and unclassified	12	9	4	25
		Total	75	40	23	138
59.9767	C_2HCl	R + CCl=CH + X	1		2	3
60.0033	C_2H_4S	Cyclic sulfides, H + (SC_2H_4) + OR, etc.	4		1	5
60.0211	$C_2H_4O_2$	$HOOCCH_2$ + R + H (rearr.)	8	6	2	16
		H + R + CH_2COO + R' + H (rearr.)	2		1	3
		R + OCH_2CH_2O + R?		3		3
60.0449	C_2H_6NO	$HOCH_2CH_2NH$ + COR, $H_2NCH_2CH(OH)$ + R			3	3

m/e	Formula	Structural Significance	Relative Probability 1	2	3	4	Total
60.0857	$H_5B_5 + H_6B_4B^{10}$, etc.						
		B_5H_{11}	1				1
		P.I.D. and unclassified	2	5	6		13
		Total	18	14	15		47
60.9845	C_2H_2Cl	C_2H_2Cl∤Y_2R, C_2H_2Cl∤Y (Y= X, NO_2)	5	1	5		11
61.0009	CH_5OSi	H_3C∤$Si(CH_3)O$‡$(CH_3)(Y)$‡H_2 (Y = R, $-CH_2COR$) (rearr.)?		2	1		3
61.0112	C_2H_5S	CH_3SCH_2∤R	8				8
		$HSCH(CH_3)-R$, R∤$CH(CH_3)S$∤R'∤H (rearr.)	3	4	2		9
		$HSCH_2CH_2$∤OR	2				2
		R-S-R (R > C_3 or subst. C_2), (rearr.) etc.	3	1	3		7
61.0289	$C_2H_5O_2$	CH_3COO∤R‡H_2 (rearr.)		4	3		7
		Other	1	3			4
61.0453	C_3H_6F		1	2			3
61.0935	$B_5H_6 + B_4B^{10}H_7$, etc.						
		B_5H_{11}		1			1
		P.I.D. and unclassified	4	1			5
		Total	27	17	16		60
61.9475	P_2	P_4		1			1
61.9923	C_2H_3Cl	Y∤(C_2H_3Cl)∤Y' (Y= mainly Cl, Y'= X, -OH, -COR, -CXRH)	4	5	3	3	15
62.0156	C_5H_2	Ph-Y_3 (Y= I, $-NO_2$, $-COOCH_3$, -NHR)		2		1	3
62.0190	C_2H_6S	C_2H_5S∤R∤H (rearr.)?			1	2	3
62.0242	CH_4O_2N	H_2NCOO∤C_2H_3‡H_2 (rearr.)		1			1
62.0367	$C_2H_6O_2$	C_2H_5OO∤C_2H_4∤H (rearr.)				1	1
62.1013	$B_5H_7 + B_4B^{10}H_8$, etc.						
		B_5H_9, B_5H_{11}			1	1	2
		P.I.D. and unclassified	2	1	1		4
		Total	6	10	6	8	30

m/e	Formula	Structural Significance	Relative Probability 1	2	3	4	Total
62.9358	SiCl	Cl ╪ SiCl ╪╪ $(CH_3)_2$			1		1
62.9638	COCl	ClCO ╪ Y (Y= X, -OR, -RX, etc.)	2	2	3		7
62.9705	CFS				1		1
62.9904	CH_3SO	CH_3-SO ╪ CH_3	1				1
63.0001	C_2H_4Cl	ClC_2H_4 ╪ Y, (Y= X, -RX, -COR, -OCOR, P, S, etc.)	14	5	4		23
		Cl ╪ C_2H_3Cl ╪ R ╪ H, etc. (rearr.)	1	1	1		3
63.0046	C_2HF_2	C_2HF_2 ╪ X		1	1		2
63.0082	CH_3O_3	H ╪ R ╪ OCOO ╪ R ╪╪ H_2 (rearr.)			1		1
63.0234	C_5H_3	Y-Ph-Z_n (Y= -OH, Z= -X,-NO_2, -OH), $n = 1\text{-}3$			6		6
		Total	18	9	18		45
63.9619	SO_2	R ╪ SO_2 ╪ X, R ╪ SO_2 ╪ R', inorg. (S_2 also possible)	6		1		7
64.0079	C_2H_5Cl	CH_3CHCl ╪ COO ╪ H (rearr.)?			1		1
64.0124	$C_2H_2F_2$	X ╪ $C_2H_2F_2$ ╪ Y (Y= R, X, -RX)		1	5		6
64.0313	C_5H_4	Y-Ph-Z (Y= -OR, -NHR; Z= X, -COR, -CN; or YZ = fused heterocyclic ring, as in benzoxazole)	1	6	2		9
		P.I.D. and unclassified	6	7	1		14
		Total	13	14	10		39
65.0202	$C_2H_3F_2$		4	3			7
65.0391	C_5H_5	C_5H_6 cpds.		2	2		4
		Subst. vinyl furans		1	1		2
		$PhCH_2Y$		3	3		6
		O_2NPhY (Y= -OH, -CH_3,-CHO)		4	2		6
		Y-Ph-Z (Y = -OR, -NHR, -SR; Z= X, H)			18		18
		P.I.D. and unclassified	1	1	4		6
		Total	5	14	30		49
65.9598	H_2S_2	H ╪ R ╪ SS ╪ R' ╪ H (rearr.)?		2	1	1	4
65.9673	CClF		1		3		4
66.0469	C_5H_6	Y-Ph-Z (Y= -OR, -NHR, -SR; Z= mainly H, CH_3)		4	2	3	9
		Methyl pyridines		1	1	3	5
		Other highly unsatd. h.c.	1		1	1	3
		P.I.D. and unclassified	5	1	1	2	9
		Total	7	8	9	10	34

m/e	Formula	Structural Significance	Relative Probability 1	2	3	4	Total
66.9654	SOF	FSO ∤ (sulfuryl fluorides)			3		3
66.9751	CHClF	FClHC ∤ R, also rearr.	3	2	4		9
67.0547	C_5H_7	Alkynes, alkadienes, cyclo-alkenes, bicyclic h.c.	23	12	6		41
		R ∤ Y (R= cyclopentyl, cyclohexyl, decalinyl, etc.; Y= R', -OR')	4	7	21		32
		P.I.D. and unclassified	1	4	1		6
		Total	31	25	35		91
68.0136	C_3H_2ON	$NCCH_2CO$ ∤ OR		2	1		3
68.0500	C_4H_6N	NCC_3H_6 ∤ R		2	1		3
68.0626	C_5H_8	Cyclopentane dvts.	4	2	6		12
		Cyclohexene dvts.	4	1			5
		Cyclohexanols, others		6	2		8
		P.I.D. and unclassified	6	5	2		13
		Total	14	18	12		44
68.9952	CF_3	F_3C ∤ C=CY (vinylic)		4	2	3	9
		Other CF_3 ∤	26	6	4	3	38
		CF_3 by rearr.		6	2	7	15
69.0340	C_4H_5O	CH_3CH=CHCO ∤ OR, CH_2 = $C(CH_3)CO$ ∤ OR, cyclopropyl-CO ∤ R, 2- or 3-R-cyclohexanone	14	9		2	25
		HOC_4H_4 ∤ R (pentynols)	3				3
69.0704	C_5H_9	C=C-C (C_2) ∤ R, $C_3H_5CH(CH_3)$ ∤ R	2	9			11
		C_2-C=C-CH_2 ∤ R	3	10	1		14
		Cyclopentyl ∤ R	2	6	2	1	11
		Other C_5H_9 ∤ R	5	1	2	2	10
		Other h.c. or cpds. with h.c. moieties	15	18	17	12	62
		C_5H_9 ∤ Y (Y= X, -SR, -C(=O)R)	5			2	7
69.0875	$C_4H_{10}B$	$(C_2H_5)_2B$ ∤ R		1			1
		P.I.D. and unclassified	3	5	6	7	21
		Total	78	75	36	38	227
70.0292	C_3H_4ON	CH_3C (CN) (OH)-	1				1
70.0656	C_4H_8N	R ∤ $CH_2NHC_3H_5$ ∤∤ HOH; pyrrolidines		3	1		4
70.0782	C_5H_{10}	$(CH_3)_2$ -cyclopentyl h.c.	5	4			9
		Terminally branched-C_5H_{11}, e.g., $C_2H_5C(CH_3)_2$ - (*m/e* 71 also large)	2	3	5		10

m/e	Formula	Structural Significance	Relative Probability 1	2	3	4	Total
70.0782	C_5H_{10} (Cont'd.)						
		Other h.c.		1	3		4
		H ⫲ C_5H_{10} ⫲ Y (Y= -OR, -SR, -ONO)	2	1			3
		(Y= -OCOR, -OCOR*)	3	7	2		12
		(Y= X)	3	1	1		5
		Others	3	5	5		13
	C_5H_{10}, C_3H_4ON, C_4H_8N	unclassified		7	3		10
70.0871	$B_5B^{10}H_5$, etc. B_6H_{10}				1		1
		P.I.D. and other unclassified		6	3		9
		Total	19	38	24		81
71.0497	C_4H_7O	n-C_3H_7CO ⫲ R		2		1	3
		n-C_3H_7CO ⫲ OR	4	5	1		10
		$(CH_3)_2CHCO$ ⫲ OR		2			2
		Tetrahydrofuryl ⫲ R	5			1	6
		Methylcyclohexanols	4				4
		Mixed ROR, ROH	2	1	1	4	8
71.0860	C_5H_{11}	$C_2H_5C(CH_3)_2$-C_nH_{2n+1}	1	4	4	2	11
		$C_3H_7CH(CH_3)$ ⫲ R, $(C_2H_5)_2CH$ ⫲ R		2	7	1	10
		Other satd. h.c.		3	24	7	34
		Cpds. with satd. h.c. moieties		12	13	10	35
		C_5H_{11} ⫲ Y (Y= -CHRR', -CRR'R'')	1	3	4		8
		(Y= -COR, -COOR)			3	4	7
		(Y= -OR; -ONO)	2		1		3
		(Y= -OC(=O)R*)	3	2			5
		(Y= X)	4	4	3		11
	Also:	$B_5B^{10}H_6$, $C_2H_5B(OCH_3)$-, CH_3CO-CO-, C_3H_3S, C_4H_9N, C_3H_5NO	2	2	1	2	7
		P.I.D. and unclassified	1	3	1	5	10
		Total	29	45	63	37	174
71.9908	C_2H_2NS	$SCNCH_2$ ⫲ R, $NCSCH_2$ ⫲ R	3	2	1		6
72.0449	C_3H_6NO	$(CH_3)_2NCO$ ⫲ R	4				4
		$H_2NCOCH_2CH_2$ ⫲ R, where R large, (m/e 59 is base)		4	2		6
72.0575	C_4H_8O	$OCHCH(C_2H_5)$ ⫲ R ⫲ H (rearr.)	1	1			2
		$C_2H_5COCH_2$ ⫲ R ⫲ H (rearr.), others	2	2	5		9

m/e	Formula	Structural Significance	Relative Probability 1	2	3	4	Total
72.0813	$C_4H_{10}N$	$CH_3NHCH(C_2H_5)$ + R, $C_2H_5NHCH(CH_3)$ + R, $C_3H_7NHCH_2$ + R, R + $CH_2N(C_3H_7)$ + R' + H (rearr.)	3	4	1		8
		C_4H_9NH + COR		1	1		2
		Cpds. having more abundant $C_nH_{2n+2}N$ peak		5			5
72.1028	$B_5B^{10}H_7$,	etc. B_6H_{10}		1			1
		P.I.D. and unclassified	2	5	8		15
		Total	15	25	18		58

m/e	Formula	Structural Significance	1	2	3	4	Total
73.0289	$C_3H_5O_2$	CH_3COOCH_2 + R (?)		1	4		5
		$HOOCC_2H_4$ + R (rearr. ?) (base for R > C_6)	5	5	3		13
		1,3-Dioxolanes + (2-R)	7				7
73.0373	C_3H_9Si	$(CH_3)_3Si$ + R	6		1		7
73.0461	$C_2H_6O_2B$	$(CH_3O)_2B$ + Y (Y= R, -OR, X)	3				3
73.0527	C_3H_7ON	$(CH_3)_2NCO$ + OPhR + H (rearr.)? (*m/e* 72 is base)		1	2		3
73.0653	C_4H_9O	$HOCH(C_3H_7)$ + R, $HOC(CH_3)(C_2H_5)$ + R	1	2	3		6
		$C_3H_7OCH_2$ + R		2	4		6
		$CH_3OC(CH_3)_2$ + R, $CH_3OCH(C_2H_5)$ + R, $C_2H_5OCH(CH_3)$ + R	2	3	1		6
		$CH_3OCH_2CH(CH_3)$ + OR, $HOCH_2C(CH_3)_2$ + OR		1	1		2
		Others	1	3	2		6
73.0891	$C_4H_{11}N$	$(C_2H_5)_2N$ + CH_2PhR + H (rearr.)? (*m/e* 58, 30 larger)			3		3
		P.I.D. and unclassified	10	5	5		20
		Total	28	23	29		87

m/e	Formula	Structural Significance	1	2	3	4	Total
74.0190	C_3H_6S	HSC_3H_5 + SH_2, cyclic sulfides			1	2	3
74.0367	$C_3H_6O_2$	$HOOCCH(CH_3)$ + R + H, CH_3OOCCH_2 + R + H (rearrs.)	11	1	1		13
		CH_3COOCH_2 + RY + H (Y= -OH, -OR') (rearr.)		1		2	3
		Others			1	2	3
74.0605	C_3H_8NO	$HOC_2H_4NHCH_2$ + R, $HOCH_2C(NH_2)(CH_3)$ + R, R + $CH_2N(C_2H_4OH)$ + R' + H (rearr.), $CH_3NHCH_2CH(OH)$ + R, etc.	4	2	1	1	8
		P.I.D. and unclassified	3	5	4	2	14
		Total	18	9	8	9	44

m/e	Formula	Structural Significance	Relative Probability 1	2	3	4	Total
75.0001	C_3H_4Cl	C_3H_4Cl + R	8				8
		Cl(C=C-C) + Y (Y= -OR, $-NR_2$, -OCOR)	6	2	1		9
		C_3H_4Cl ‡ HXY (Y= X, -COR, -OCOR), C_3H_4Cl ‡ X_3	5	1	4	1	11
75.0046	C_3HF_2	$C_nH_pX_qF_2$ ($q > p$)		2	1		3
75.0166	C_2H_7OSi	$HOSi(CH_3)_2$ + R, CH_3 + $Si(CH_3)_2O$ + R + H (rearr.)?	1		1	1	3
75.0235	C_6H_3	Ph ‡ HY_2^*		1	5	15	21
75.0268	C_3H_7S	$C_2H_5SCH_2$ + R; $HSC(CH_3)_2$ + R	4			1	5
		$CH_3SCH(CH_3)$ + R, $HSCH(C_2H_5)$ + R	2	1	2		5
75.0445	$C_3H_7O_2$	$(CH_3O)_2CH$ + R	3	1	1	1	6
		$HOC_2H_4OCH_2$ + R, $HOC_2H_4CH(OH)$ + R, etc.		4	2	2	8
		C_2H_5COO + R ‡ H_2 (rearr.)			1	2	3
75.0558	$C_2H_7ON_2$	R + CH $(NHCH_2OH)$- NH + $NHCH_2O$ + H (rearr.)			1		1
		P.I.D. and unclassified	1	1	4	2	8
		Total	30	13	23	25	91
75.9441	CS_2	Thiols, sulfides, etc., prob. from cracking on M.S. filament.					
75.9999	C_2NF_2	$NCCF_2$ + X	1	1			2
76.0034	CH_2O_3N	O_2NOCH_2 + R (nitrates)				5	5
76.0080	C_3H_5Cl	C_3H_5Cl ‡ HX	1		1	3	5
		Y + C_3H_5Cl + Y' (Y= H, Cl, etc.; Y'= -COR, -OR, -OCOR, -R)	1	2	2	3	8
76.0313	C_6H_4	Ph ‡ HY*		3			3
		Y + Ph + Y' (Y, Y'= variety of substs. or Y-Y'= fused arom. ring)		1	4	11	16
		P.I.D. and unclassified	3	6	4	3	16
		Total	6	13	11	25	55
76.9794	C_2H_2OCl	$ClCH_2CO$ + Y (Y= X, -OR, R); CCl_3CH_2OH	4		3		7
77.0158	C_3H_6Cl	C_3H_6Cl + Y (Y= X, -COR, R, -OR)	7	2	4		13
77.0203	$C_3H_3F_2$	$C_3H_3F_2$ + X, $C_3H_3F_2$ ‡ HYX (Y= X, -RX)	2	1	4		7

m/e	Formula	Structural Significance	Relative Probability 1	2	3	4	Total
77.0265	C_5H_3N	Pyridyl ╪ HY*		2			2
77.0391	C_6H_5	Ph ┼ Y (Y= variety of subst.)	13	33	66		112
		o-Y-Ph-Y' (rearr.) (*m/e* 77 >> 76)	2	8	8		18
		m-, *p*-Y-Ph-Y' (rearr.) (*m/e* 77 > 76)		3	13		16
		Others (unsatd. h.c., indoles, etc.)		2	6		8
		P.I.D. and unclassified		4	7		11
		Total	28	55	111		194
78.0344	C_5H_4N	Pyridyl ┼ Y (Y= -COR, -X, -CH=CHR, -NHR, -R, etc.)	3	2	4	3	12
78.0469	C_6H_6	Ph ┼ Y.┼ H (Y= metal-R, $-NHNH_2$; unsatd. as -C=N-, -C=C-; -OR, -SR) (rearr.)	4	3	4	2	13
		YCH_2 ┼ Ph ┼ Y' (Y= -OH, -H or fused to Y'; Y'= -OH, -O-, -CO-, $-NO_2$, etc.) (rearr.)	3	1	1	7	12
		Cycloalkadienes, substd. cycloalkenes		1	2		3
		P.I.D. and unclassified	7	5	3	6	21
		Total	17	12	14	18	61
78.9671	CH_4SiCl	$(ClCH_2)_2Si(CH_3)_2$-	1				1
78.9676	CH_3S_2	CH_3SS ┼ Y (Y= CH_3, $-SCH_3$)		1	1		2
78.9751	C_2HClF	C_2HClF ┼ Cl			1		1
78.9949	CH_4O_2P	$OPH(OCH_3)$ ┼ OCH_3, CH_3O ┼ $PO(CH_3)O$ ┼ CH_3 (rearr.)		2			2
78.9950	C_2H_4OCl	$ClCH_2OCH_2$ ┼ R, $Cl\overset{O}{\overset{\|}{C}}$ ┼ OC_2H_3Cl ┼ R ┼ H (rearr.)	1	1			2
79.0422	C_5H_5N	Pyridyl-Y ┼ H (rearr.) (Y= -COR, -CH=CH-)	1	2	1		4
		Pyridyl- $(CH_3)_n$		1	5		6
79.0547	C_6H_7	Cycloalkadienes, alkenynes	5				5
		Cyclohexenyl ┼ Y, cyclopentenyl ┼ Y (Y= -COR, $-CH_2OH$, -CH=CHR, -CN, -R); polycycloalkenes, -anes	4	5	3		12
		Ph ┼ CH (OH) Y (rearr.) (*m/e* 79 > *m/e* 77, *m/e* 107 usually > *m/e* 79); PhCH (NH_2) Y (rearr.)	1	7	1		9

m/e	Formula	Structural Significance	Relative Probability 1	2	3	4	5	Total
79.0547	C_6H_7 (Cont'd.)							
		Y-Ph-Y' (Y= H, Y'= -OCOR, -OR; Y= CH_3, Y'= -X, $-CH_2X$; Y= $-CH_2OH$, Y'= X) (rearr.)		3	7			10
		P.I.D. and unclassified	3	5	10			18
		Total	16	27	29			72
79.9754	CH_4S_2	$CH_3SS \nmid R \nmid H$ (rearr.)	1			1		2
80.0027	CH_5O_2P	$CH_3OOPH \nmid OCH_3$ (rearr.)	1					1
80.0262	C_5H_4O?	Methylhydroxybenzenes			2		1	3
80.0500	C_5H_6N	Alkylpyrroles, subst. pyridines and anilines		8	4	4	1	17
80.0626	C_6H_8	Subst. cyclohexenes		1	2	2		5
		Cyclohexyl-YY', -YY'Y'' (Y= X, OH, *t*-bu, etc.)	1	1	1		2	5
		Satd. multiple fused ring cpds.	1	1			3	5
		P.I.D. and unclassified	3	7	4	2	1	17
		Total	7	18	13	9	8	55
80.9907	C_2H_3ClF	$C_2H_3ClF \nmid Y$	3					3
81.0340	C_5H_5O	Furan-$CH_2 \nmid R$	5		2			7
		HOPhY (Y= -OR, $-NH_2$)			5			5
81.0578	C_5H_7N	Pyrrole-$CH_2 \nmid R \nmid H$ (rearr.); R-pyridine-NH_2	1	1	1	1		4
81.0704	C_6H_9	Alkyl hexynes; hexadienes	2	5	4	1		12
		Cyclohexenyl $\nmid$ Y, polyisoprenes	7	2	3	1		13
		Cyclohexyl $\not\parallel$ HYZ (mainly Y= -OH, Z= R, or YZ= fused ring)	10	16	9	6		41
		Cyclohexyl-Y, -YY'Y'', etc.	4	4	6	1		15
	Also: $HOCH_2CF_2$-, CH_3OCF_2-, BCl_2, $CHF_2CO \nmid OR \nmid H_2$ (rearr.)		3	1		1		5
		P.I.D. and unclassified	1	2	5	6		14
		Total	36	31	35	17		119

m/e	Formula	Structural Significance	Relative Probability 1	2	3	4	5	Total
81.9377	CCl_2	CCl_2 ⫲ XY (Y= $-CH[OR]_2$, -CHO, -CN, X, etc.)	3	2	2	2		9
82.0656	C_5H_8N	$NCCH_2CH_2CH_2CH_2$ + R	1		1			2
82.0782	C_6H_{10}	Cyclohexyl ⫲ HY (Y= R, substd. R; -OR, X, etc.)	8	19	7	8		42
		Cyclohexyl ⫲ YZ (mainly Y= -OH, Z= R) etc.		2	3	4		9
		P.I.D. and unclassified	4	6	5	8		23
		Total	16	29	18	22		85
82.9455	$CHCl_2$	$CHCl_2$ + Y	12	3	4	4		23
		Cl + CCl_2 + CO-R + H (rearr.), (impurity?)	2	2	3	4		11
82.9603	SO_2F	FSO_2 + Y (Y= X, -OR)	4		1	1		6
82.9955	C_4H_3S	Thiophene + Y (Y= X, -COR)		1	1	1		3
83.0108	$C_2H_2F_3$	$C_2H_2F_3$ + Y	1	4	2			7
83.0297	C_5H_4F	F-Ph-Y (Y= -OH, -OR, R, $-NH_2$)		3	4	1		8
83.0497	C_5H_7O	Dihydropyrans, alkenones, alkynols, etc.	3	1	2			6
83.0860	C_6H_{11}	Cyclohexyl + Y (Y= R, X, etc.)	20	18	7	14		59
		Other cycloalkyl cpds.; olefins	9	7	3	5		24
		Alkyl-Y, -YY' (Y= -OH, X)	5	2	4	4		15
		P.I.D. and unclassified	3	2	4	3		12
		Total	59	43	35	36		174
84.0034	C_4H_4S	Thiophene + C_2H_2 + H (rearr.)					1	1
84.0375	C_5H_5F	F-Ph-Y (Y= $-NH_2$, -OR) (*m/e* 83 large)		1	2			3
84.0813	$C_5H_{10}N$	Piperidines, methyl pyrrolidines, imidazolines (rearr.)	6		1	1		8
84.0938	C_6H_{12}	Alkanes (*m/e* 85 large)		1	2	2	2	7
		C_6H_{12} ⫲ HY (Y= X, -OCOR, -SH, etc.), C_6H_{12} ⫲ (OH) ($-CH_2OH$)	3	1		4	1	9
		Others	2	1	1	3		7
		P.I.D. and unclassified	2	6	9	12	11	40
		Total	13	12	16	24	16	81
84.9621	SiF_3		1					1
84.9655	POF_2			1				1
84.9657	$CClF_2$	$CClF_2$ + (rearr.)	19	5	13			37
85.0289	$C_4H_5O_2$		1	2				3

m/e	Formula	Structural Significance	Relative Probability 1	2	3	4	5	Total
85.0653	C_5H_9O	C_4H_9CO ∤ R, C_4H_9CO ∤ OR	1	3				4
		Cyclopentanols, others	1	1	4			6
85.0765	$C_4H_9N_2$	Piperazine ∤ R		1	1			2
85.0891	$C_5H_{11}N$			1	1			2
85.1017	C_6H_{13}	$C_3H_7C(CH_3)_2$ ∤ R, $CH_3C(C_2H_5)_2$ ∤ R		4				4
		$C_4H_9CH(CH_3)$ ∤ R, $C_3H_7CH(C_2H_5)$ ∤ R		6	3			9
		Other satd. h.c., etc.		1	3			4
		C_6H_{13} ∤ Y (Y= -COR, -COOR)		2				2
		(Y= -OCOR*)		2	1			3
		(Y= -OR)	2	2				4
		(Y= X)		4				4
		P.I.D. and unclassified		16	6			22
		Total	25	51	32			108
86.0731	$C_5H_{10}O$	$CH_3COC(CH_3)_2$ ∤ R ∤ H, $C_3H_7COCH_2$ ∤ R ∤ H (rearrs.)		1			1	2
		RO ∤ $C_5H_{10}O$ ∤ H, etc.	3	4	2	3	2	14
86.0969	$C_5H_{12}N$	$(C_2H_5)_2NCH_2$ ∤ R, $C_3H_7NHCH(CH_3)$ ∤ R, $C_4H_9NHCH_2$ ∤ R, etc.	14	2	1		1	18
		R ∤ $CH_2N(C_4H_9)$ ∤ Y (Y= RCO-, $PhCH_2$-) (rearr.)	3					3
		Others	1				2	3
		P.I.D. and unclassified	5	7	3	5	5	25
		Total	26	14	6	8	11	65
87.0001	C_4H_4Cl	C_4H_4Cl ∤ X, C_4H_4Cl ‡ HX_2, C_4H_4Cl ‡ H_2X_3	1		1	2		4
87.0268	C_4H_7S	Thiacycloalkanes	3					3
87.0446	$C_4H_7O_2$	C_3H_5COO ∤ R ‡ H_2 (rearr.)		3	1	3		7
		$CH_3OOCC_2H_4$ ∤ Y, CH_3OOC-cyclohexyl-Y (rearr.)	3	8	3		1	15
		$CH_3COOCH(CH_3)$ ∤ R		3	1		1	5
		Other esters and acids	3			1	2	6
		Methyl dioxolanes, etc.	4	1	2	1		8
87.0530	$C_4H_{11}Si$	$C_2H_5(CH_3)_2Si$ ∤ R			1		1	2
87.0616	$C_3H_8O_2B$	C_3H_7OB(∤OR) -O ∤ R ∤ H (rearr.)	2					2
87.0809	$C_5H_{11}O$	ROCR'R'' ∤ Y (ΣR= C_4H_{11}, Y= R, -OR)		6	4	2	2	14
		HOCRR' ∤ Y (ΣR= C_4H_{10})		2	3	1	2	8

m/e	Formula	Structural Significance	Relative Probability 1	2	3	4	5	6	Total
87.1047	$C_5H_{13}N$	$(C_2H_5)_2NCH_2$ ╪ R ╪ H (rearr., 86 is larger)		1			2		3
		P.I.D. and unclassified	3	16	9	9	5		42
		Total	19	40	25	19	16		119
88.0398	$C_3H_6NO_2$	$CH_3OOCCH(NH_2)$-, $CH_3OOCCH(NH$ ╪ COR) ╪ R' ╪ H (rearr.)	1	2	1	1	1		6
88.0524	$C_4H_8O_2$	$C_2H_5OCOCH_2$ ╪ Y ╪ H (rearr.) (Y= R, -OR, -COOR)	1		1	1	2		5
		$HOOCCH(C_2H_5)$ ╪ R ╪ H (rearr.)		2					2
		Others				1	1		2
88.0762	$C_4H_{10}NO$	Z ╪ CYNY'Y'', Z ╪ CYN (Y') ╪ Z' ╪ H (rearr.) (ΣY= C_3H_9OH, Z= -R, $-CR_2OH$, etc.)	4	2	2	4	1		13
		P.I.D. and unclassified	2	2	4	1	2		11
		Total	8	8	8	8	7		39
89.0158	C_4H_6Cl	C_4H_6Cl ╪ X	2	3					5
89.0322	C_3H_9OSi	RCH_2OSiR_3, $ROCH_2SiR_3$ (rearrs.)		1	1	1	3		6
89.0391	C_7H_5	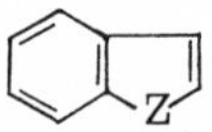 (Z= S, -NH-, $-CH_2$-), PhCHYY', $YPhCH_2Y'$, $PhCH_2Y$, $YPhCH_3$, Y_3-(Ph-C) (Y=X, -CN, $-NO_2$, etc.)		1	3	7	7	22	40
89.0425	C_4H_9S	$C_3H_7SCH_2$ ╪ R	2	1			1		4
89.0602	$C_4H_9O_2$	$(CH_3O)_2C(CH_3)$ ╪ Y (Y= -OR, R), $HOC_3H_6OCH_2$ ╪ R, $HOC_2H_4OC_2H_4$ ╪ OR, etc.		3	1	5	4	2	15
		C_3H_7COO ╪ R ╪╪ H_2 (rearr.)			2	2	1		5
		P.I.D. ions		3	2	5	7	1	18
		Other unclassified	2		1	2	1	1	7
		Total	6	12	10	22	24	26	100

m/e	Formula	Structural Significance	1	2	3	4	5	6	7	8	Total
90.0344	C_6H_4N	YPhNCO, $YPhNHCONH_2$, YPhNHR (Y= $-NO_2$, X)		3	1	1	1	1		1	8
90.0469	C_7H_6	$PhCH_2Y$*, CH_3PhY*, benzo cpds., etc.		4	6	3	4	4	5	8	34
	Also:	C_4H_7Cl ǂ HX, $C_4H_{10}S$, $C_4H_{10}O_2$			1	1	1	1			4
		P.I.D. ions	1	3	1	3	1	2	1	1	13
		Other unclassified			1	1	1				3
		Total	1	10	10	9	8	8	6	10	62
91.0314	C_4H_8Cl	ClC_4H_8 + R; ClC_4H_8 + OR	7		1						8
91.0422	C_6H_5N	PhN ǂ HY; Y + PhNH + Y'	3	3	3						9
91.0547	C_7H_7	$PhCH_2$ + Y (Y= -OR, R, X, -RX, -COR etc.)	48	18	5						71
		CH_3Ph + Y*, CH_3Ph + CH_3	13	11	11						35
		PhCH ǂ YY' + H, PhC ǂ Y_3 ǂ H_2 (rearrs.) (Y= R; X, -OR)	18	9	7						34
		Combinations of above (rearr.), etc.	2	7	27						36
	Also:	$ClCH_2CH_2CO$ + OR, $(NO_2)_2$ + PhO + R	1	1	3						5
		P.I.D. ions			6						6
		Other unclassified	2	5	1						8
		Total	94	54	64						212
92.0262	C_6H_4O	HOPhY (Y= $-NO_2$, -COOR, large R, X, -OH, etc.)		3	2	4					9
92.0500	C_6H_6N	PhNH + Y (Y= -COR, $-NH_2$), H_2NPh + Y (Y= X, -COR, -COOR)		2	4	5					11
		CH_3-pyridyl + Y (Y= $-CH_3$, -COR, H), pyridyl-CH_2 + R		1	2	5					8
92.0626	C_7H_8	$PhCH_2$ + R + H, $PhCH_2$ + RY + H (rearrs.)	12	7	5	4					28
		$PhCH_2$ + OR + H, $PhCH_2$ + NRY + H, $PhCH_2$ + SR + H (rearrs.)	1	5	4	9					19
		$PhCH=CHCH_2OR$, (rearr.), α-pinene, etc.	1	2		1					4
		P.I.D. ions	4	1	1	4					10

m/e	Formula	Structural Significance	Relative Probability				Total
			1	2	3	4	
92.0626	C_7H_8 (Cont'd.)						
		Other unclassified	1	4		7	12
		Total	19	25	18	39	101
92.9340	CH_2Br	$BrCH_2$ ┼ Y (Y= X, R, -RX, etc.)		3		7	10
92.9952	C_3F_3	Halocarbons and dvts.	5		8	5	18
93.0107	C_3H_6OCl	Cl (C_2H_5) C (OH) ┼ R, $ClC_2H_4OCH_2$ ┼ R	3	1			4
93.0340	C_6H_5O	HOPh ┼ Y (Y= $-NR_2$, -COR, $-NO_2$, X)		1	5	3	9
93.0578	C_6H_7N	Pyridyl-CH_2 ┼ R ┼ H; Y ┼ pyridyl-CH_2 ┼ R (rearrs.)	2		1	2	5
		PhN(┼R) ┼ Y, PhNH ┼ Y (rearrs.) (Y= -COR, -N=CR, -NHR, R), N-Ph-dihydro-benzoxazines	5	3	3	5	16
93.0704	C_7H_9	Terpenes ($C_{10}H_{16}$); cyclohexenyl-Y_2, $-Y_3$; sesquiterpenes	12	4	1	1	18
	Also:	C_3H_3ClF, $C_2H_2O_2Cl$, RPO (OR) OCH_3 (rearr.), $Cl(CH_3)_2$ Si ┼ R	2	2	2	2	8
		P.I.D. ions	6	4	1	2	13
		Other unclassified		1	1		2
		Total	35	19	22	27	103
93.9419	CH_3Br	$BrCH_2$ ┼ Y ┼ H, R ┼ BrCH ┼ Y [Y= -COOH, -COH, -Ph (X) NO_2] (rearrs.)	5				5
94.0418	C_6H_6O	PhO ┼ Y ┼ H (Y= R, -COR, -RY') (rearr.)	15	6	5	1	27
		Y* ┼ PhO ┼ Y, HOPh ┼ Y, benzopyrans (rearrs.)				5	5
	Also:	C_2H_5SS ┼ R ┼ H (rearr.), HOOCCHCl ┼ R ┼ H (rearr.), $CH_3PO(OCH_3)$ ┼ OR ┼ H (rearr.) C_7H_{10}, C_3HF_3, Cl_2C=C ┼	6	3	3	1	13
		P.I.D. ions	5	1			6
		Other unclassified		2	2		4
		Total	31	12	8	9	60

m/e	Formula	Structural Significance	Relative Probability 1	2	3	4	5	6	Total
95.0133	$C_5H_3O_2$	Furyl-CO ∤ Y (Y= -OR, R); furyl-CH(OCOR)$_2$	7	4	1				12
95.0497	C_6H_7O	$PhOH_2$? [from $PhOC(CH_3)_3$, $(CH_3)_3CPhOH$, $Ph(OCH_3)_2$, ROPhYY' (Y= X, -CHO)]		2	2	3	2		9
		Methylfurans, cyclohexenones, etc.		3		1	2		6
95.0860	C_7H_{11}	Dienes, cycloalkenes, dicyclo-alkanes, etc.	9	7	5	7	5		33
	Also:	$C_3H_2F_3$, C_3H_5ClF, FPh ∤ Y*, -HSeCH$_2$-, CH_3OSO_2 ∤ OR, C_2HCl_2-, CH_3-pyrazole-CH_2-	5	4	4	3	3		19
		P.I.D. ions	1	2	3	9	7		23
		Other unclassified	1			1	2		4
		Total	23	22	16	24	21		106
96.0938	C_7H_{12}	Dicycloalkanes, cycloalkyl ‡ HY (Y= -OH, R) etc.	3	6	5	5	2	1	22
	Also:	$C_2H_2Cl_2$, furyl-CHO ‡ YY', $C_5H_{10}CN$, FPh ∤ R ∤ H (rearr.), $C_3H_2F_3$	3	4		5	2	4	18
		P.I.D. ions	4	10	4	3	7	1	29
		Other unclassified	1		1		1	2	5
		Total	11	20	10	13	12	8	74
96.9612	$C_2H_3Cl_2$	$C_2H_3Cl_2$ ∤ Y (Y= X, -RX, -NO_2, -R, -COOR)	6	2	4	6			18
97.0112	C_5H_5S	Thiophene-CH_2 ∤ R	8		3	2			13
97.1017	C_7H_{13}	$CH_3C_6H_{10}$ ∤ Y, alkenes, C_7H_{13} ‡ HY_2	12	11	4	7			34
	Also:	C_6H_9O, CF_3CO-	1	1					2
		P.I.D. ions				2			2
		Other unclassified			3	5			8
		Total	27	14	14	22			77

m/e	Formula	Structural Significance	Relative Probability						
			1	2	3	4	5	6	Total
98.0969	$C_6H_{12}N$	CH_3-piperidyl +, etc.	5		2		1		8
	Also:	$C_6H_{10}O$ (cyclohexanols,etc.), furfuryl alkanoates, C_2HClF_2, C_7H_{14}, thiophene-CH_2 + R + H (rearr.), piperazine ‡ R_2	1	6	2	3	3		15
		P.I.D. ions	2	4	10	3	12		31
		Other unclassified	2		1	3	4		10
		Total	10	10	15	9	20		64
98.9813	$C_2H_2ClF_2$		1	2	1	1		1	6
98.9846	H_4O_4P	H_2 ‡ R + OPO (O + R + H)$_2$ (rearr.)	1	1					2
99.0082	$C_4H_3O_3$	Maleates, fumarates	1	1	1				3
99.0446	$C_5H_7O_2$	$CH_3COC_2H_4CO$ + R, $CH_3COOC_3H_4$ + R		3		1			4
99.0809	$C_6H_{11}O$	1,1-cyclohexyl = $(OCH_2)_2$, CH_3-tetrahydropyran + OR, $C_5H_{11}CO$ + R, $C_5H_{11}CO$ + OR	3			1		1	5
99.1173	C_7H_{15}	RR'R"C + C_nH_{2n+1} (R, R', R" not = H, $\Sigma R = C_6H_{15}$)					1	2	3
		Other satd. h.c.				1			1
		C_7H_{15} + Y (Y= X, -COOR)		3				1	4
	Also:	Imidazolone-CH_2-, $C_6H_{13}N$, C_5H_4Cl (ClPhXNH$_2$, ClPhXOH), Cl_2SiH + R, $C_5H_{11}N_2$ (methylpiperazines), S_2Cl, SO_2Cl	1		7	3	2	3	21
		P.I.D. and other unclassified	1	6	6	6	6	4	29
		Total	8	16	15	13	9	12	78
99.9936	C_2F_4	Perfluoroalkenes, -cycloalkanes	1	1	2	2	2		8
		Others				1	3	6	10
100.0080	C_5H_5Cl	Cl-Ph-Y (Y= -OR, -SR)					2	2	4
100.0762	$C_5H_{10}NO$	$(C_2H_5)_2$ NCO + R			2	1			3
		4-R-morpholines	4				2		6
100.0888	$C_6H_{12}O$	Cyclohexyl-O + R + H (rearr.), RO + $C_6H_{12}O$ + H, etc.	1		2	1		1	5
100.1126	$C_6H_{14}N$	RR'NCR"R''' +, where $\Sigma R = C_5H_{14}$	1	5					6
		Other amines, mainly (n-$C_4H_9)_2$-NCH_2CHROH		2	1	1			4

m/e	Formula	Structural Significance	1	2	3	4	5	6	7	Total
100.1126	$C_6H_{14}N$	(Cont'd.)								
		RCO ǂ N (C_5H_{11}) CH_2 ǂ R (rearr.)	2							2
		Unclassified	1	3	2	3	4	7		20
		Total	10	11	9	9	13	16		68
100.9361	CCl_2F		16	1	3	3	5			28
101.0391	C_8H_5	Styrene ǂ HY_2 (Y= X, -NO_2)	1				1			2
101.0425	C_5H_9S	Thiacyclohexanes, methylthiacyclopentanes, etc.	4	1	1					6
101.0602	$C_5H_9O_2$	ROCR'R" ǂ Y (ΣR= C_4H_9O), etc.	2	2		2				6
		$C_2H_5COOC_2H_4$ ǂ, $C_2H_5OCOC_2H_4$ ǂ, etc.	3	2		1				6
101.0966	$C_6H_{13}O$	ROCR'R" ǂY, HOCRR' ǂY (ΣR=C_5H_{13})		1	3	1	1			6
	Also:	PCl_2, PSF_2, $CH_3SiC_4H_9$-, C_2HF_4, C_2H_5OB (C_2H_5) O-, $(C_2H_5O)_2B$-, C_5H_6Cl, CF_3S, and $C_5H_{13}N_2$	5	1	4					10
		Unclassified	1	9	2	6	10			28
		Total	32	17	13	13	17			92
102.0469	C_8H_6	Quinolines (loss of RCN), etc.; PhC_2H ǂ YY', YY' ǂ PhC_2H_3 ǂ HY, etc. (Y= X, -NO_2, -CN, H, R)		2	2	4	1	7	6	22
102.0680	$C_5H_{10}O_2$	Ester, etc., rearrs. (see *m/e* 74, 88)			2		2			4
	Also:	CF_3CON (C_2H_5) ǂ R ǂ H_2 (rearr.), R ǂ PhCN, $C_2(CN)_3$-		1	1		1			3
		Unclassified	1	4	2	3	—	1	—	11
		Total	1	7	7	7	4	8	6	40

m/e	Formula	Strucutral Significance	Relative Probability 1	2	3	4	5	Total
103.0394	$C_4H_7O_3$	$CH_3COOCH_2CH_2CH_2(OH)$ ∤ R		2	1	1	1	6
103.0479	$C_4H_{11}OSi$	$(CH_3)_3SiCH_2O$ ∤ R, $(CH_3)_2Si(OC_2H_5)$ ∤ OR?		2		1		3
103.0547	C_8H_7	PhC_2H_2 ∤ Y (Y= $-CO_2R$, -COR, X, R); highly unsat. h.c.; PhCHCH (∤ Y) ∤ O, 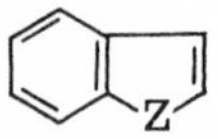 (Z= NH, O, =C=O),	1	6	5	1	9	22
		PhC_2H_2∤∤HYY', Y∤PhC_2H_3-∤∤HY' (Y = X, -OR, R), etc.		4	5	11	9	29
103.0581	$C_5H_{11}S$	$C_3H_7SCH(CH_3)$ ∤ R, etc.		1	1		2	4
103.0758	$C_5H_{11}O_2$	$HOC_3H_6OCH(CH_3)$ ∤ R, $(C_2H_5O)_2CH$ ∤ OR etc.		6	4	2	1	13
		P.I.D. ions	1	17	1	3	3	25
		Other unclassified			3	1	1	5
		Total	2	38	20	20	26	106

m/e	Formula	Strucutral Significance	1	2	3	4	5	Total
104.0262	C_7H_4O	Y ∤ PhCO ∤ Y' (Y= -COR, $-NO_2$, H; Y'= -OR, R, X)	3	5	5		4	17
104.0500	C_7H_6N	Ph - N(CH∤∤) ∤, pyridyl-C_2H_2-, CPhN	1	1	3	2	1	8
104.0626	C_8H_8	Tetralins, indanes, Ph-cycloalkenes, -anes, $PhCHYCH_2Y'$ (Y or Y'= X, -OH, -OCOR, Ph, R, H), etc.	11	8	13	4	5	41
	Also: C_5H_9Cl, C_4H_8OS		1		1			2
		P.I.D. ions	3	7	2	4	4	20
		Total	19	21	24	10	14	88

Subtotal, m/e 1-104, 2335 2312 2503 732 313 120 17 10 8342

m/e	Formula	Structural Significance	1	2	3	4	5	6	7	8	Total
105.0340	C_7H_5O	PhCO+Y (Y= R, -OR, -OCOR, X, etc.)	34	2							36
		Y_nPhCO-Y'(rearr.), $PhCH_2O$-Y, Y_n-PhOH, etc.	1	9	5						15
105.0704	C_8H_9	PhCH (CH_3) + Y, CH_3PhCH_2 + Y (Y= R, X, -OR, etc.), C_2-Ph + Y (Y= X, CH_3)	4	5	6						15
		PhCh=CH+CH_2OR - +H_2 (rearr.), others	8	15	13						36
	Also:	C_7H_7N, C_2H_2Br, $C_3H_2O_2Cl$	4	4	1						9
		P.I.D. ions	5	1							6
		Other unclassified	4	1	4						9
		Total	60	37	29						126

m/e	Formula	Structural Significance	1	2	3	4	5	6	7	8	Total
106.0418	C_7H_6O	HO(CH_3) Ph(+ H) + Y*, HOPh(+H)CH_2+Y (Y = OH, -$CONH_2$, Ph)		3	2						5
106.0656	C_7H_8N	H_2NPhCH_2 + Y, etc.	6	3	1						10
		PhNHCH_2 + Y; H + R +NHPhCH_2 - + Y (rearr.)	10	2							12
		YCO +NHPhCH_2+ R (Y= R, -RZ) (rearr.)	13	3	3						19
		CH_3-pyridyl-CH_2 + R, etc.	3	9	1						13
		PhCH_2NH-, PhCH (NH_2) +, H_2N (CH_3)Ph + X, PhN (CH_3) + COR, Ph-lactams, etc.	7	3							10

m/e	Formula	Structural Significance	Relative Probability 1	2	3	4	5	Total
106.0782	C_8H_{10}	CH_3PhCH ǂ Y ǂ H, PhC (cyclo-R) ǂ Y ǂ H, PhCH (CH_3) ǂ Y ǂ H (rearrs.)	1	6	6			13
	Also:	C_2H_3Br ǂ XY, C_2H_3Br ǂ Hy, Pyridyl-CO-	1	3	2			6
		P.I.D. ions	3	6	3			12
		Other unclassified	4	2	1			7
		Total	48	40	19			107
107.0497	C_7H_7O	$HOPhCH_2$ ǂ Y (Y= R, -COR); HOPhC ǂ R_3, HOPhCH ǂ R_2 (rearrs.)	4	8	7			19
		$HOPh(CH_3)$ ǂ Y*, Y ǂ $OPh(CH_3)$ ǂ Y* (Y= R, -RY') (rearr.); CH_3PhO ǂ RY (108 is larger)	2	8	5			15
		Y ǂ $OPhCH_2$ ǂ Y' (Y= R, -COR, X) (rearr.); $PhOCH_2$ ǂ Y (Y= -COR, -RX; 94 is large)	5	2	7			14
		PhCH (OH) ǂ RY; $PhCH_2O$ ǂ RY, Y ǂ OCH_2Ph ǂ Y' (rearr.), X ǂ $PhCH_2OH$	9	8	4			21
	Also:	C_2H_4Br, $C_3H_4O_2Cl$, C_7H_9N, $HSC_2H_4OC_2H_4$ ǂ OR, linolenic acid, $ClCH_2Si(CH_3)_2$ ǂ R, $C_6H_7N_2$	4	9	7			20
		P.I.D. ions	12	4	2			18
		Other unclassified	2	3	1			6
		Total	38	42	33			113
108.0449	C_6H_6ON	H_2NPhO ǂ C_2H_5, RCO ǂ NHPhO ǂ R' (rearr.), pyridyl-CHOH ǂ	5	2				7
108.0575	C_7H_8O	CH_3PhO ǂ Y ǂ H (Y= R, -COR, -RY') (rearr.)	3	4	1			8
		$PhCH_2O$ ǂ Y ǂ H (Y= -COR, $-CH_2C_2H_3$) (rearr.), $PhOCH_2$ ǂ ROH (rearr.), C_2 -quinones		2	1	3	2	7

m/e	Formula	Structural Significance	Relative Probability 1	2	3	4	5	6	7	Total
108.0575	C_7H_8O (Cont'd.)									
	Also:	C_6H_4S (benzothiazoles, HSPh + Y), BrC_2H_4 + COOR (rearr.), C_3H_7SS + R + H (rearr.), R-pyrroles		3	2	2	1			8
		P.I.D. ions	9	5	3	4	5			26
		Other unclassified	1	2	1	1	3			8
		Total	18	17	8	10	11			64
108.9612	$C_3H_3Cl_2$	$C_3H_3Cl_2$ + HX_2, $C_3H_3Cl_2$ + X	6	1	1					8
109.0289	$C_6H_5O_2$	HOPhO + R, CH_3 + OPhO + R + H (rearr.), CH_3-furyl-CO-	1	4		2				7
109.0449	C_6H_7ON	H_2NPhO + Y + H, HOPhNH + Y + H (Y= R, -COR) (rearrs.)	1	1	3					5
109.1016	C_8H_{13}	See C_7H_{11} (*m/e* 95)	4	1	3					8
	Also:	C_3ClF_2, PhS +, $FPhCH_2$ +, R + PO (OC_2H_5) -O + R + H (rearr.), ClPh ‡ HX_2, C_7H_9O	7	7	6					20
		P.I.D. ions	4	4		2				10
		Other unclassified	2			2				4
		Total	25	18	13	6				62
110.0367	$C_6H_6O_2$	HOPhO + R + H, HOPh(+Y)-O+R (rearrs.)	3		1	1	1			6
110.1094	C_8H_{14}	$C_6H_{11}C_2H_3$ (+ H) + OR, etc.	2	2	1	1	2		2	10
	Also:	$C_7H_{10}O$, ClPh ‡ YY', C_2H_5Se + R + H (rearr.) $C_3H_4Cl_2$, CBrF	1	2	3	3				9
		P.I.D. ions	5	8	4	2	5	1	4	29
		Other unclassified	1		2	2	3		2	10
		Total	12	12	11	9	11	1	8	64

m/e	Formula	Structural Significance	Relative Probability 1	2	3	4	5	Total
111.0001	C_6H_4Cl	ClPh ǂ Y*, ClPh (ǂY) ǂ -CHROH (rearr.)	2	6	10	5		23
111.0268	C_6H_7S	CH_3-thiophene-CH_2 ǂ R	9		1	3		13
111.0446	$C_6H_7O_2$	Adipates (RO ǂ COC_4H_7CO ╪ (H) OR?), etc.	2	1	2	1		6
	Also:	C_8H_{15} , $C_3H_5Cl_2$, $(CH_3)_2$-boroxin ǂ R, $C_3H_2ClF_2$, CHBrF, $C_7H_{11}O$, $OP(OCH_3)_2$ ǂ R ╪ H_2, thiophene-CO ǂ	11	5	7	12		35
		P.I.D. ions	1	2	1	1		5
		Other unclassified			5	2		7
		Total	25	14	26	24		89
112.0160	$C_5H_4O_3$	Furan-COO ǂ R ǂ H (rearr.) (*m/e* 95 is base), etc.	1	3				4
112.1126	$C_7H_{14}N$	CH_3-piperidine-CH_2 ǂ R, cyclohexyl-N (ǂ R ǂ H) -CH_2 ǂ R, etc.	2	2				4
112.1251	C_8H_{16}	H ǂ C_8H_{16} ǂ Y (Y= -OCOR, -OH; R)			1	3	3	7
	Also:	FPhO ǂ R ǂ H (rearr.), ClPh ǂ Y* ǂ H (rearr.), C_3F_4 , -COC_4H_8CO-, etc.	5	1	3	2	1	12
		P.I.D. ions	6	7	2	7	8	30
		Other unclassified			1			1
		Total	14	13	7	12	12	58
112.9281	CH_3SiCl_2	CH_3SiCl_2-, H ǂ R ǂ CH_2SiCl_2 ǂ (rearr.)	4	1			2	7
113.0014	C_3HF_4		2	1				3
113.0238	$C_5H_5O_3$	Furyl-COO ǂ R ╪ H_2 (rearr.), $CH_3OOCCH{=}CHCO$-			3		1	4
113.0966	$C_7H_{13}O$	Cyclic ethers, $C_6H_{13}CO$-		1		1		2
113.1329	C_8H_{17}	C_8H_{17} ǂ X				1	1	2
	Also:	$(CH_3)_2$-piperazine-, CHBrF, F_2Ph-, C_2H_2F, CF_3S-, C_2ClF_2O, $C_2H_3Cl_2O$	1	1	3	2	1	8

m/e	Formula	Structural Significance	Relative Probability 1	2	3	4	5	6	Total
113.1329	C_8H_{17} (Cont'd.)								
		P.I.D. ions			3	4	2		9
		Other unclassified	5	1		5	6		17
		Total	12	5	9	13	13		52
114.0918	$C_6H_{12}ON$	HO - RN(CH_2 ∤) C_2H_2R' ∦ HOH (ΣR= C_3H_7)			2				2
114.1282	$C_7H_{16}N$	See $C_6H_{14}N$ (*m/e* 100)	3	4		1		2	10
		P.I.D. ions	1	1	1	3	4	2	12
		Other unclassified		1	3			1	5
		Total	4	6	6	4	4	5	29
115.0547	C_9H_7	Indenes, $(CH_2=CH-)_2Ph$		2		1			3
		Naphthyl-Y (Y= -OR, $-NR_2$, R)		6	6	3	2		17
		PhC_3H_4Y, PhC_3H_3YY'', indanyl-Y, $YPhC_3H_4Y'$ (Y= X, -OCOR, $-NO_2$, Ph, R, etc.)	4	5	18	13	4		44
		Ph-Ph-Y (Y= -OR, $-NO_2$, -OCOR), Ph-R-Z, etc.			1	6	12		19
115.0758	$C_6H_{11}O_2$	Aliphatic esters, etc. (see $C_5H_9O_2$)	1	1		2			4
115.0996	$C_6H_{13}ON$	$C_4H_{10}NCOCH_2$ ∤ R ∤ H (rearr.)	2	1		1			4
115.1122	$C_7H_{15}O$	ROC (R'R'') ∤ Y, HOCRR' ∤ Y (ΣR=C_6H_{15})	1		1	1			3
	Also: $C_2H_2Cl_2F$, C_8H_5N					1	1		2
		P.I.D. and other unclassified	1	6	6	5	3		21
		Total	9	21	31	34	22		117
115.9641	C_2ClF_3		1		1			1	3
116.0500	C_8H_6N	Y ∤ CH_2PhCN, PhCH(CN) ∤ Y, Y ∤ $PhCH_2CN$, PhCYY'CN (rearr.) (Y= R, X)	2	4	1	1	2		10
116.0626	C_9H_8	PhC_3H_3 ∦ HY, PhC_3H_3 ∦ YY' (Y= X, R, $-NO_2$, $-NH_2$), etc.	1	1	1		6	5	14

m/e	Formula	Structural Significance	Relative Probability 1	2	3	4	5	6	Total
116.0626	C_9H_8 (Cont'd.)								
		Naphthyl-Y (Y= -NHR, -OR); quinaldines			1	3	2	2	8
116.1075	$C_6H_{14}NO$	Amino alcohols, ethers				2		1	3
		P.I.D. and other unclassified	5	2	5	3	4	3	22
		Total	9	7	9	9	14	12	60
116.9066	CCl_3		11	5	6	1			23
117.0704	C_9H_9	CH_3 (PhC = C) ⫲ Y, $C_2H_3PhCH_2$ ⫲ Y, PhCH=$CHCH_2$ ⫲ Y, indanyl ⫲ Y (Y= R, X, -COOH, etc.)	17	7		6			30
		($Ph-C_3$) ⫲ HYY'; (PhC_3) ⫲ H_2Y (Y= X, R, -OR, etc.)	1	2	3	5			11
117.0915	$C_6H_{13}O_2$	See $C_5H_{11}O_2$ (*m/e* 103)			4				4
	Also:	$POCl_2$, C_2HClF_3, C_5F_3, $C_4H_5O_4$ (maleate)	1	1	3	1			6
		P.I.D. ions	5		2	2			9
		Other unclassified		1	1	3			5
		Total	35	16	19	18			88
118.0782	C_9H_{10}	PhC_3H_5 ⫲ HY (Y= OR; R, fused ring), PhC_3H_5 ⫲ YY (Y= R, X); Y ⫲ $CH_2PhC_2H_4$ ⫲ Y'	2	1	6	1	4	2	16
	Also:	C_8H_6O (misc.), C_8H_8N (misc.); $C_5H_{12}O_2N$	2		3	1	2	6	14
		P.I.D. ions	7	8	1	2	5	2	25
		Other unclassified		1	4	2	2		9
		Total	11	10	14	6	13	10	64
118.9920	C_2F_5	(*m/e* 69 usually base peak)		8	1				9
119.0497	C_8H_7O	CH_3PhCO ⫲ Y; dihydrobenzofuran ⫲ Y	5	2	2				9
		Others		4	3				7

m/e	Formula	Structural Significance	Relative Probability 1	2	3	4	Total
119.0860	C_9H_{11}	RPhC(R')⫲Y ($\Sigma R = C_2H_7$), Ph $(CH_3)_4$	21	7	6		34
		Others (multiple cleav., rearr.) (see C_8H_9)	1	5	5		11
	Also:	C_3H_4Br, C_7H_5ON, CH_2Cl_3, $C_7H_3O_2$	5	1	1		7
		P.I.D. ions	1	13	7		21
		Other unclassified	1	2	5		8
		Total	34	42	30		106
120.0211	$C_7H_4O_2$	Y⫲OPhCO⫲Z (Y= H, -COR, R; Z= -OR, H); dihydro-coumarins	9	3		2	14
120.0449	C_7H_6ON	H_2NPhCO⫲R, Y⫲PhNHCO⫲R, (rearr.), *o*-H⫲CH_2PhNO⫲O, H_2NPhCO⫲Y	3	1	1	2	7
120.0575	C_8H_8O	$PhCOCH_2$⫲R⫲H (rearr.), PhC-(C-OH)⫲YH, HOPh (cyclo-R)⫲Y, $PhOC_2$⫲HY		2	6		8
120.0813	$C_8H_{10}N$	See C_7H_8N (*m/e* 106)	16	7	4	1	28
120.0938	C_9H_{12}	C_2Ph⫲Y⫲H, CPhC (CH_3)⫲Y⫲H(rearrs.)			2	1	3
	Also:	C_2HOBr ($CH_2BrCOOR$), $PhSi(CH_3)$⫲RR', C_3H_5Br, $CH_2ClCOOCH(CH_3)$-	3	1	1	1	6
		P.I.D. ions	2	7	7	4	20
		Other unclassified	2		1	2	5
		Total	35	21	16	19	91
120.9289	C_2H_2OBr	$BrCH_2CO$⫲Y (Y= -OR, R)	2	4			6
121.0289	$C_7H_5O_2$	HOPhCO⫲Y (Y= R, Ph, H, -OR); O_2N⫲PhCOO⫲R (rearr.), OHCPhO⫲R	6	4	7		17
121.0653	C_8H_9O	See C_7H_7O (*m/e* 107)	8	10	15		33
	Also:	$C_8H_{11}N$, C_3H_6Br, C_9H_{13} (some monoterpenes, dvts.), $(CH_3O)_3Si$-, $ClC_3H_6OC_2H_4$-, ferrocene	6	7	3		16

m/e	Formula	Structural Significance	Relative Probability 1	2	3	4	5	6	Total
121.0653	C_8H_9O	(Cont'd.)							
		P.I.D. ions	7	9	6				22
		Other unclassified	2	1	2				5
		Total	31	25	33				99
122.0367	$C_7H_6O_2$	PhCOO ∤ R ∤ H; R'OOC ∤ PhCOO ∤ R(rearrs.)		2		1	2		5
122.0731	$C_8H_{10}O$	See C_7H_8O; HOPhCH(CH_3) ∤ R ∤ H (rearr.)	4	1	1	1	1		8
	Also:	C_7H_8ON, O_2NPh ∤ CHO, R-pyrroles, C_4H_9SS ∤ R (rearr.), C_2H_3OBr	4		1	1	1	1	8
		P.I.D. ions	6	11	9	2	5	4	37
		Other unclassified		2	1			2	5
		Total	14	16	12	5	9	7	63
123.0446	$C_7H_7O_2$	PhCOO ∤ R ‡ H_2 (rearr.); $(HO)_2PhCH_2$ ∤ R, $CH_3OPh(OH)$ ∤ Y		4	3	2	1		10
123.0809	$C_8H_{11}O$	Sesquiterpenones, etc.	2	1	1	1	2		7
	Also:	$C_4H_5Cl_2$, C_9H_{15}, C_3HOCl_2, CH_3OPhNH ∤ (rearr.), C_2HBrF, O_2NPh ∤ Y ∤ H (Y= -COOH, -OCH_3) (rearr.), $PhCH_2S$ ∤	5	5	4	1	1		16
		P.I.D. ions		5	5	2	2		14
		Other unclassified	1			3	3		7
		Total	8	15	13	9	9		54
124.	C_9H_{16}, CH_3PhCl ‡ Y_2, $C_7H_8O_2$, $C_8H_{12}O$, H_2NPhCl ‡ HY_2		3	2	1	2	2	3	13
		P.I.D. ions	4	3		5	4	3	19
		Other unclassified	1	1	1			1	4
		Total	8	6	2	7	6	7	36

m/e	Formula	Structural Significance	Relative Probability					
			1	2	3	4	5	Total
125.0158	C_7H_6Cl	$ClPhCH_2$ ∤ Y (Y= R, X), Cl (CH_3) Ph ∤ Y (Y=X, $-NO_2$), PhCHCl ∤ R, etc.	16	5	4			25
		Also: $(CH_3)_2$-thiophenyl-CH_2 ∤ etc., $C_4H_7Cl_2$, C_3Cl_2F, $C_2H_3Cl_2CO-$	7	6	4			17
		P.I.D. ions		3				3
		Other unclassified	4	1	5			10
		Total	27	15	13			55
126.		$ClPhCH$ ‡ R_2 ∤ H, C_2H_5-thiophene-CH_2 ∤ R ∤ H, $ClPhCH_2$ ∤ R ∤ H (rearrs.), naphthyl ‡ HY (Y= X, -COOH)	2		1	2	3	8
		P.I.D. ions	3	10	3		1	17
		Other unclassified	2	2	1	2	3	10
		Total	7	12	5	4	7	35
126.9049	I	Iodo compounds		6	3	3		12
127.0188	C_6H_6NCl	ClPhNH ∤ COY ∤ H (rearr.) (see C_6H_7N)	4	2	1			7
127.0359	$C_7H_5F_2$	$PhCF_2$ ∤ R, CHF_2Ph ∤ R	2		1			3
127.0547	$C_{10}H_7$	Naphthyl ∤ Y (Y= X, -COOH, -COOR)		3	5	3		11
		Also: $C_2H_5OCOC_2H_2CO-$, SF_5, ClPhO ∤ R, $C_3H_3Cl_2O$, H ∤ R ∤ OPO (OC_2H_5) O ∤ R ‡ H_2 (rearr.)	2	4	2	1		9
		P.I.D. ions		6	6	4		16
		Other unclassified	6	1	1	5		13
		Total	14	22	19	16		71
128.		$C_8H_{18}N$ (see $C_6H_{14}N$), C_6H_5OCl [ClPhO ∤ R ∤ H, HOPh (Cl) ∤ Y (rearrs.)], $C_{10}H_8$, C_9H_6N (quinolines)	6	4	6	7		23

m/e	Formula	Structural Significance	Relative Probability 1	2	3	4	5	6	Total
128.	$C_8H_{18}N$ (Cont'd.)								
		P.I.D. ions	6	2	5	3			16
		Other unclassified			1	2			3
		Total	12	6	12	12			42
128.8931	$CHBr^{81}Cl$	$CHBr^{81}Cl$ ‡ Y, (Y= X, R)	1		2	1		1	5
128.9152	$CBrF_2$	$CBrF_2$ ‡ Y (Y= X, R)	3	1	2	1	1	1	9
128.9719	C_3HClF_3	C_3HClF_3 ‡ Y (Y= X, R), etc.	3		2				5
129.0551	$C_6H_9O_3$	RO ‡ COC_4H_8COO ‡ R ‡ H (rearr.) (adipates)	5	1					6
129.0704	$C_{10}H_9$	Indenes, R-Ph-R (R= unsatd., cyclic) etc.			4		1		5
		Indanes, tetrahydronaphthalenes					2	6	8
129.0915	$C_7H_{13}O_2$	Esters, acids, etc. (see $C_5H_9O_2$)		1	2	1		1	5
129.1279	$C_8H_{17}O$	HOCRR' ‡ Y ($\Sigma R = C_7H_{16}$)	1			1		1	3
	Also:	C_9H_7N, $-CH_2OSO_2Cl$, C_2Cl_3, $(C_3H_7O)_2B-$;	3		2			1	6
		P.I.D. and other unclassified	6	5	2	5	3	5	26
		Total	22	8	16	9	7	16	78
130.0656	C_9H_8N	Indole-CH_2 ‡, methylindole ‡ Y, $C_2H_5C(Ph)(CN)$ ‡ R	5	3	1			1	10
130.0782	$C_{10}H_{10}$	Ph-butenes, CH_3-indanes, cyclohexyl-Ph-, etc.	1	1	3	2	1	1	9
130.1231	$C_7H_{16}NO$	Amino alcohols	1	1					2
	Also:	C_2HCl_3, $C_3H_2ClF_3$	2					1	3
		P.I.D. ions	7	9	2		6	4	28
		Other unclassified	1	1	3	3	1	3	12
		Total	17	15	9	5	8	10	64
130.9920	C_3F_5		5	4	4	4			17
131.0497	C_9H_7O	PhCH=CHCO ‡ Y (Y= R, -OR); (PhO) C_3H_x	10	2	1	2			15

m/e	Formula	Structural Significance	1	2	3	4	5	Total
131.0860	$C_{10}H_{11}$	Tetrahydronaphthyl-, methylindanes, $(CH_3)_2(PhC{=}C)$ ǂ Y (Y= R, X, etc.); (PhC_4) ⧧ HY_2	9	1	9	6		25
	Also:	$C_2H_2Cl_3$, C_4H_4Br, $C_5H_{11}O_2Si$, $C_5H_{15}Si_2$, $C_7H_{15}O_2$	3	3	1	6		13
		P.I.D. ions		7	5	5		17
		Total	27	17	20	23		87
132.0575	C_9H_8O	(PhC(C)—O—C) ⧧ YY', 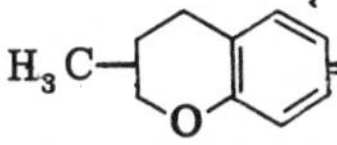 ⧧ YY', C=C-CPh (OH) ⧧ YY' (Y= X, -COOR, R, H)	1	3	1	1	1	7
132.0813	$C_9H_{10}N$	$(C{=}CPhCNH_2)$ ǂ Y, (CPhN-C-C) ǂ Y, (NPhCC=C) ǂ Y etc. (Y= X, -COR, R)	3	2	1	1		7
132.0938	$C_{10}H_{12}$	$(CH_3)_2PhCHCH_2$ ⧧ HOH, Tetralins, etc.	2	1	1	3		7
	Also:	C_8H_6NO, $C_2Cl_2F_2$, $C_6H_{14}O_2N$, C_5H_7ONCl, $C_8H_4O_2$, $C_6H_2Cl_2$	1	2	2	4	3	12
		P.I.D. ions	7	15	4	2	5	33
		Total	14	23	9	11	9	66
133.0653	C_9H_9O	C_2-PhCO ǂ Y; 2,3-dihydrobenzopyran ǂ Y, etc.	5	1	1			7
		$PhOC_3H_4$ ǂ Y, cyclohexyl-PhO ǂ Y, C_3H_5PhO ǂ Y, etc.	8	8	4			20
133.1017	$C_{10}H_{13}$	RPhC(R'R'') ǂ Y ($\Sigma R{=}C_3H_9$)	12	6	2			20
		Others (mult. cleav., rearr.) (see C_8H_9)		5	1			6
	Also:	C_8H_7ON (acetanilides), $C_8H_5O_2$ (phthalides, etc.), $C_5H_{13}O_2Si$, C_4H_6Br, CF_3S_2, $C_3H_2F_5$, $C_9H_{11}N$, $C_2HCl_2F_2$	7	7	1			15

m/e	Formula	Structural Significance	Relative Probability 1	2	3	4	5	6	Total
133.1017	$C_{10}H_{13}$	(Cont'd.)							
		P.I.D. ions	2	10	3				15
		Other unclassified	1	1	3				5
		Total	35	38	15				88
134.0064	C_7H_4NS	Benzothiazole ∤ Cl				1			1
134.0605	C_8H_8ON	*o*-H ∤ C_2H_4PhNO ∤ O, PhN (CH_3) CO ∤ R, CH_3CONHPh ∤ Y	1		2				3
134.0731	$C_9H_{10}O$, $C_8H_6O_2$,	H ∤ OPh (CH_3) CO ∤ OR, H ∤ (PhCH_2O) C_2H_3 ∤ OCOR, etc.	2	3		1	1		7
134.0969	$C_9H_{12}N$	See C_7H_8N	6		2	5	2		15
		P.I.D. ions	4	17	14	8	2		45
		Other unclassified		2	8	1			11
		Total	13	22	26	16	5		82
134.9810	C_4H_8Br	BrC_4H_8 ∤ R (R > CH_3), BrC_4H_8 ∤ X	9	3	1				13
135.0446	$C_8H_7O_2$	CH_3OPhC(=O) ∤ Y, HOPh (-CHO) CH_2 ∤ Y, HOOCPhCH_2 ∤, etc.	6	3	1				10
135.0683	C_8H_9ON	PhN ($COCH_3$) ∤ R ∤ H (rearr.), PhN ($COCH_2$ ∤ R) ∤ R' (rearr.) [PhN (CHR ∤ R') ∤ COR" larger]		7	4				11
135.0809	$C_9H_{11}O$	See C_7H_7O; PhOC (C_2H_6) ∤, PhCH_2OCH (CH_3) ∤	13	3	7				23
	Also:	PhSi $(CH_3)_2$ ∤, Cl_3Si ∤, C_2ClF_4, $[(CH_3)_2N]_2$PO ∤ NR_2	5	3					8
		P.I.D. ions	4	9	5				18
		Other unclassified	3		1				4
		Total	40	28	19				87

m/e	Formula	Structural Significance	1	2	3	4	5	6	Total
			Relative Probability						
136.0080	C_8H_5Cl	Cl-$(PhC_2)\nmid$Z (Z= Y_4, HY_2CH_3, Y_2, HY; Y= X, $-NO_2$)			1		4	2	7
136.1251	$C_{10}H_{16}$	Decahydronaphthyl- (137 is large), etc.	1	2	1	1	1	1	7
	Also:	(see *m/e* 122) $C_9H_{12}O$, $C_8H_{10}ON$, $C_8H_8O_2$, $C_8H_{12}Si$, $C_5H_{12}S_2$, C_3H_5OBr	5	4	1	2	6	2	20
		P.I.D. ions	3	11	5	2	4	4	29
		Other unclassified					1		1
		Total	9	17	8	5	16	9	64
137.1329	$C_{10}H_{17}$	Decahydronaphthyl-; etc.	7		1	2			10
	Also:	$C_8H_9O_2$, Ph (Cl) (C=C)-, $BrC_2H_4OCH_2$-, $C_5H_7Cl_2$, $C_8H_{11}ON$	2	2	3	6			13
		P.I.D. ions	2	15	7	3			27
		Total	11	17	11	11			50
138.		HOOCCHBr$\nmid$R$\nmid$H, HOPhCOO$\nmid$R$\nmid$H (rearrs.), $CH_3PhCCl\nmid X_2$, etc.		1	7	2	4		12
		P.I.D. ions	2	4	1	4	5		16
		Other unclassified	2	1	1		1		5
		Total	4	6	9	6	8		33
138.9950	C_7H_4ClO	ClPhCO$\nmid$Y (Y= R, H, -OR)	8		1				9
139.0314	C_8H_8Cl	See C_7H_6Cl	13	1	5				19
	Also:	$C_{11}H_7$, C_3H_7-thiophene-CH_2-, C_3H_5BrF, $C_2H_5COCCl_2\nmid X$	4	2	2				8
		P.I.D. ions	1	2	1				4
		Other unclassified	1	2	1				4
		Total	27	7	10				44

m/e	Formula	Structural Significance	Relative Probability 1	2	3	4	5	Total
140.0267	C_7H_7NCl	$ClPhNHCH_2$ ∤ R, ClPhN(∤COR)-CH_2∤R (rearr.)	5	1	2	1	1	10
	Also:	C_7H_5OCl [CH_3OPhCl ‡ HX, HOPh(Cl)CH‡R_2], $C_6H_{11}NR_2$, CHI	1	1		2	3	7
		P.I.D. ions	1	16	7	3	6	33
		Other unclassified		1				1
		Total	7	19	9	6	10	51
141.0704	$C_{11}H_9$	Naphthyl-CH_2 ∤ R, etc.	7	5	1			13
		PhOPhY (Y= H, X), PhPhOY (Y= H, R, -COR), O=C(OPh)$_2$ (rearrs. - loss of CO?)		3	10			13
	Also:	C_7H_6OCl (see C_7H_7O), CH_2I; $PhSO_2$-, C_2H_3ClBr, $(C_4H_9)_2Al$-	3	5	3			11
		P.I.D. ions	2	17	7			26
		Other unclassified	2	2	2			6
		Total	14	32	23			69
142.0078	$C_{11}H_{10}$	Naphthyl-CH_2 ∤ R ∤ H (rearr.); PhOPh etc. (rearrs.) (see $C_{11}H_9$)		1	4	2		7
142.0185	C_7H_7OCl	See C_7H_8O (*m/e* 108)	3			1		4
142.1595	$C_9H_{20}N$	See $C_6H_{14}N$ (*m/e* 100)	6		2	1		9
		P.I.D. ions	7	3	4	8		22
		Other unclassified				3		3
		Total	16	4	10	15		45
142.9222	$C_3H_2Cl_3$	$C_3H_2Cl_3$ ∤ X, $C_3H_2Cl_3$ ∤ HX_2	3	1				4
142.9920	C_4F_5	C_4F_5 ∤ X, C_4F_5 ∤ OR	2	2		3	1	8
143.0860	$C_{11}H_{11}$	See $C_{10}H_9$ (*m/e* 129)		1		2	1	4
	Also:	$C_2H_2BrF_2$, $C_4H_3ClF_3$, $C_2H_3Br^{81}Cl$, $CH_3OOC(CH_2)_6$ ∤ R, naphthyl-O ∤	4	1	2	2	2	11

m/e	Formula	Structural Significance	Relative Probability 1	2	3	4	5	Total
143.0860	$C_{11}H_{11}$ (Cont'd.)							
		P.I.D. ions	4		2	7	2	15
		Other unclassified	2	1	2	2	2	9
		Total	15	6	6	16	8	51
144.	Naphthyl-O † Y † H (rearr.) (Y= R, salicyl); CH_3-indole-CH_2 †, $C_8H_{18}NO$ (amino alcohol), Cl_2Ph ‡ $(NO_2)_2$, C_3OClF_3, PhC (CN) (C_2H_5) †		6	1	1	2	1	11
		P.I.D. ions	2	1	2	7	6	18
		Other unclassified				1	1	2
		Total	8	2	3	10	8	31
144.9612	$C_6H_3Cl_2$	Cl_2Ph † Y (Y= $-NO_2$, X, -COR)		2		8		10
145.1017	$C_{11}H_{13}$	See $C_{10}H_{11}$, *m/e* 131	7	1	1			9
	Also: PhC(CN) (C_2H_5) † R † H (rearr.) $C_3H_4Cl_3$, CF_3Ph † X, $CH_3COOCH_2CH(OOCCH_3)$ -		4	1	7	1		13
		P.I.D. ions	1	6	3	3		13
		Other unclassified	3	4		4		11
		Total	15	14	11	16		56
146.0731	$C_{10}H_{10}O$	† C_3-PhCO † Y (Y= OH, -CHClR, etc.)	3		1	1		5
	Also: $C_{11}H_{14}$ (145 or 147 larger), O_2N † $PhCl_2$ † R ‡ H_2 (rearr.)			3	2	1	1	7
		P.I.D. ions	8	7	6	1	3	25
		Other unclassified	1	2	1		1	5
		Total	12	12	10	3	5	42

m/e	Formula	Structural Significance	Relative Probability 1	2	3	4	5	Total
146.9625	C_3ClF_4		6	1	1	2		10
147.0461	$C_5H_{15}Si_2O$	$(CH_3)_3SiOSi(CH_3)_2$- (often formed in inlet from other trimethylsilanes) (148, 66, 73 often large)	4					4
147.0809	$C_{10}H_{11}O$	See C_9H_9O (*m/e* 133)	1	2	6	3		12
147.1173	$C_{11}H_{15}$	See $C_{10}H_{13}$ (*m/e* 133)	13	3	1			17
	Also:	Benzothiophene -CH_2 ⫲, $CH_3COPhCO$-, $CBr^{81}ClF$, C_2F_5-CO ⫲	5		4	1		10
		P.I.D. ions		2	2	1		5
		Other unclassified	1		1	1		3
		Total	30	8	15	8		61
148.0524	$C_9H_8O_2$	PhCH=CHCOO ⫲ R ⫲ H (rearr.) (133 is base peak)		2	1		1	4
	Also:	$C_{10}H_{14}N$, $C_{10}H_{12}O$, CH_2=CHPh(NO_2)-, C_2Cl_3F	1	2	1	1	3	8
		P.I.D. ions	3	19	10	6	5	43
		Other unclassified		1	1	1	1	4
		Total	4	24	13	8	10	59
149.0238	$C_8H_5O_3$	Phthalates; terephthalates [RO ⫲ COPhCOO ⫲ R ⫲ H (rearr.)]; HOOCPhCO ⫲ Y	11	3				14
149.0966	$C_{10}H_{13}O$	(See C_7H_7O, *m/e* 107)	3	2		2		7
	Also:	$C_9H_9O_2$ (see *m/e* 135), $CH_3PhSi(CH_3)_2$-, $H_2NPhN(C_2H_5)CH_2$-, $C_{10}H_{12}ON$ (see *m/e* 135), R ⫲ CH_2OSi-$(OC_2H_5)_2$ ⫲ OR (rearr.), FSO_3CF_2-, C_4H_6OBr	4	5	2	2		13
		P.I.D. ions	1	7	6	2		16
		Other unclassified	2	1		1		4
		Total	21	18	8	7		54

m/e	Formula	Structural Significance	1	2	3	4	5	6	7	8	Total
150.0191	$C_7H_4NO_3$, $C_8H_8NO_2$	O_2NPhCO ∤ Y (see C_7H_5O); O_2NPhCH (CH_3) ∤	9	2							11
	Also:	NCS-PhO ∤ CH_3			1						1
		P.I.D. ions	2	12	11	10					35
		Other unclassified		3	3						6
		Total	11	17	15	10					53
		Subtotal, *m/e* 1-150	3217	3114	3167	1135	538	197	25	10	11403
150.9329	$C_2Cl_2F_3$		3	4	3	2					12
151.0758	$C_9H_{11}O_2$, $C_8H_7O_3$	$(HO)_2$PhC $(CH_3)_2$-, $(CH_3O)_2$ PhCH_2-, CH_3O (HO) PhCO-, CH_3OOCPhO-, etc.	4		3		1				8
	Also:	IC≡C-, CH_2=CH(CH_3)-PhCl ∤ Cl, mono-terpenones, $C_{12}H_7$		1	3		3				7
		P.I.D. ions	2	3	1		2				8
		Other unclassified		3		1					4
152.0626	$C_{12}H_8$	Ph_2 ∦ Y [Y= X_2, $(OH)_2$, O=C ∦, R, -OR], PhCHRPh		3	4	5					12
	Also:	CH_3O-$C_7H_5O_2$ (see $C_7H_6O_2$), O_2N (HO) PhCH_2-, CH_2=CHCON-(cyclo-hexyl)-, Cl-benzox-azolyl	2	2	1						5
		P.I.D. ions	3	5	8	2					18
		Other unclassified	2			2					4

m/e	Formula	Structural Significance	Relative Probability 1	2	3	4	5	Total
153.0471	$C_9H_{10}Cl$	See C_7H_6Cl	5		2	1	1	9
153.0704	$C_{12}H_9$	PhPh + Y (Y= $-NO_2$, X, R); (naphthyl-C=C) + R_2 + H (rearr.)	1	2		2	2	7
		Also: BrC_2H_4COO + R + H_2 (rearr.), $TiCl_3$, $(CH_3O)_2PhO$ +, $CH_3OPhCOO$ + R + H_2, thiophene-$COCH_2CO$ +	3		2			5
		P.I.D. ions	2	5	3	4	2	16
		Other unclassified	2	1			1	4
154.		$HCONHPhCl$-, Ph_2SiCl_2, (rearr.), $CF_3CON(C_2H_5)CH_2$-, C_8H_7OCl (see C_7H_5OCl)	2	1	1	2	3	9
		P.I.D. ions	3	6	6	4	1	20
155.		C_8H_8OCl (see C_7H_7O), BrPh + Y (see Ph + Y), $C_7H_4O_2Cl$ (see $C_7H_5O_2$), $(C_2H_5O)_2POO$ + C_2H_3 + H_2, H + R + O- (C_4H_9O-) POO + R + H_2, etc. (rearrs.), $C_3H_3Br^{81}Cl$, C_5F_5, $C_3H_2BrF_2$, $PhPO(OCH_3)$-, naphthyl-CO-, CH_3PhSO_2-, $H_9C_4OOCC_2H_2CO$-, $(pyridyl)_2$-, CH_3-naphthyl-CH_2-, $C_{11}H_{23}$ + CH_2NH_2	11	8	11	4		34
		P.I.D. ions		8	4	3		15
156.		$C_8H_{17}N(CH_3)CH_2$-, etc., CH_3-quinoline-CH_2-, etc., Br-pyridyl + X, $(H_9C_4)_2NCO$ + R	1	1	1	3		6
		P.I.D. ions	7	7	3	3	4	24
		Other unclassified					2	2

m/e	Formula	Structural Significance	Relative Probability 1	2	3	4	5	Total
156.9244	$C_3H_5Br^{81}Cl$		4			1		5
156.9465	$C_3H_4BrF_2$		1			1		2
	Also:	H + $ROOCCH_2$ + C ($COOC_4H_9$) = CHCO + OR ‡ H_2 (rearr.)?, $(C_3H_7)_3Si$ + SiR_3, 1-Ph-(CH_3) = pyrazole + X	1	2				3
		P.I.D. ions	3	8	4	8		23
158.0969	$C_{11}H_{12}N$	$(CH_3)_2$-indole-CH_2-	1	1				2
158.1095	$C_{12}H_{14}$	H + (Ph) -cyclohexyl + OR (R= -C_2H_4OH, H)	1	1			1	3
		P.I.D. ions	5	3	4	2	3	17
		Other unclassified	2	1			3	6
158.9768	$C_7H_5Cl_2$	Cl_2PhCH_2 +, $PhCCl_2$ + X; $Cl_2PhC(CH_3)_3$	10			1		11
	Also:	$C_{12}H_{15}$, C_6H_8Br-, CHFI-	2	1	1			4
		P.I.D. ions		4	3	4		11
		Other unclassified	1	2	1	4		8
160.	C_2BrF_3, CH_3O-indole-CH_2 +, Cl + Cl_2PhO + H		1	1			1	3
		P.I.D. ions	4	9	4	2	1	20
		Other unclassified				3		3
161.1329	$C_{12}H_{17}$	See $C_{10}H_{13}$ (*m/e* 133)	8	2	2			12
	Also:	$C_{11}H_{13}O$, CH_3-benzothiophene-CH_2 +, BrC_6H_{10} +, C_3H_5CON (Ph) + R + H (rearr.)	2	2		2		6

m/e	Formula	Structural Significance	Relative Probability 1	2	3	4	Total
161.1329	$C_{12}H_{17}$	(Cont'd.)					
		P.I.D. ions	2	15		3	20
		Other unclassified		1	3	6	10
161.9639	$C_6H_4OCl_2$	Cl_2PhO + Y + H (rearr.) (Y= R, -COR, CH_3SO_2-)	9	3	1		13
		Also: PhN (C_4H_9) -CH_2 +, PhN ($COCH_3$) $CHCH_3$ +	1		1	1	3
		P.I.D. ions	7	16	11	7	41
		Other unclassified			1	2	3
162.9329	$C_3Cl_2F_3$		7		4	1	12
163.1122	$C_{11}H_{15}O$,	$C_{10}H_{11}O_2$, $C_9H_7O_3$ (see *m/e* 149)	5		2	3	10
		Also: $C_{12}H_{19}$, $CBr^{81}Cl_2$, $(C_2H_5O)_3Si$-, $C_4H_4ClF_4$, C_3OClF_4, $C_{10}H_{13}ON$	4	3	4		11
		P.I.D. ions	1	4	4	4	13
		Other unclassified	3	1	3	1	8
164.		C_6H_{11}-C_6H_9 ‡ HOH, $C_3H_5(CH_3O)$ PhO ‡ R- ‡ H (rearr.), OHC (CH_3O) PhO ‡ R - ‡ H (rearr.), H + fluorene + CN	2		1	2	5
		P.I.D. ions	7	19	9	4	39
		Other unclassified	3		2	1	6
165.0704	$C_{13}H_9$	Y-PhCHZPh-Y', *ar*–Ph-Z-CH_3-benzofurans, YPh-Ph(Y')-CH_3 (Y=Y=X, -ORX, -OH; if Y= R, 167, 166, or 168 larger) (Z= R, X)		4	15	5	24
165.0915	$C_{10}H_{13}O_2$, $C_9H_9O_3$	See *m/e* 151	4	3			7

m/e	Formula	Structural Significance	Relative Probability 1	2	3	4	5	Total
165.0915	$C_{10}H_{13}O_2$ (Cont'd.)							
	Also:	$CH_2BrCOOCHCH_3$ +, ClPhCH=CHCO +, Cl-benzo-furan-CH_2 +, $(H_5C_2O)_2OPC_2H_4$ +, C_5Cl_3	2	2	5	3		12
		P.I.D. ions	1	6	7	3		17
		Other unclassified				2		2
166.0782	$C_{13}H_{10}$	$(Ph_2C)YY'$ (Y= X, OH, Ph, R)	1		2	2	2	7
	Also:	$C_2Cl_3Cl^{37}$, (C_3H_5PhOCl) ‡ X_2, carbazole +, O_2N (HO) PhCO +, Ph (COO + R + H)$_2$ (rearr.), ClPhN (C_3H_5) + COR	2	2	4	1	2	11
		P.I.D. ions	5	6	3	7	4	25
		Other unclassified	1			1	3	5
166.9034	$C_2Cl_3F_2$		1	1	2	2		6
167.0860	$C_{13}H_{11}$	Ph_2CH + R, $PhPhCH_2$ + R, acenaphthenes	7	5				12
	Also:	ClPhN $(CH_2CH{=}CH_2)$ + COR + H (rearr.), $C_{10}H_{12}Cl$, Cl (HO) PhC_3H_4 ‡ C_3H_7, H + R + OOCPhCOO + R + H_2 (rearr.), $C_2HCl_3Cl^{37}$	4	1	2	2		9
		P.I.D. ions	2	3	1	2		8
		Other unclassified	2		5	3		10
168.		(Ph_2O) ‡ Y (Y= Cl_2, CO, COR+ X, etc.), (Ph_2N) + Y (Y= R, -COR), C_9H_9OCl (see C_7H_5OCl), O_2NPh + NO + O (rearr.), $C_8H_8O_4$ (see $C_7H_6O_2$)	4	5	4	2		15
		P.I.D. ions	8	6	6	7		27
		Other unclassified			2			2

m/e	Formula	Structural Significance	Relative Probability 1	2	3	4	5	Total
168.9653	C_7H_6Br	See C_7H_7	4			7		11
169.0420	$C_9H_{10}OCl$	See C_7H_7O	4	2				6
169.0653	$C_{12}H_9O$	PhPhOǂ; PhOPhǂY, $HOPh_2$-ǂY (Y=X, -OPh, etc.)	6	8	3	2		19
	Also:	Ph_2NǂCORǂH (rearr.), ClPhSi $(CH_3)_2$-, naphthyl-C_3-, $Cl_2C_2H_3COOCH(CH_3)$-, $H_5C_3OOCC_4H_8CO$-, Cl-terpenols, C_3F_7; $ClCH_2CON$ (Ph) ǂRǂH (rearr.), etc. (see $C_9H_{10}ON$), $C_{12}H_{25}$, Br (HO) Ph‡X_3	5	4	6	5		20
		P.I.D. ions	3	6	5	2		16
		Other unclassified	1		2			3
170.0731	$C_{12}H_{10}O$	PhPhOǂYǂH (Y= R, -COR) (rearr.)	10	1	4			15
		$(H_{11}C_5)_2NCH_2$ǂ, BrPhNH-ǂCOR, $(pyridyl)_2$N-, C_3H_7-(Cl) PhOǂROǂH (rearr.)	4		1	1		6
		P.I.D. ions	5	9	5	9		28
		Other unclassified	1		1			2
170.9768	$C_8H_5Cl_2$	Cl_2PhC_2‡HX_2, Cl_2Ph (C=C)ǂX	1	1	1			3
171.0809	$C_{12}H_{11}O$	Ph-Ph-OǂYǂH_2 (Y= -R-OH, $-COCH_3$, R) (rearr.)	1	2	1	1		5
	Also:	ROǂ$COC_7H_{14}COO$ǂRǂH (rearr.), FPhPhǂH, C_5ClF_4, CH_3OPhSO_2ǂX	1	1	1	1		4
		P.I.D. ions	3	14	2	4		23
		Other unclassified	1	1	2	1		5
171.9524	C_6H_5OBr	BrPhOǂYǂH (rearr.) (Y= R; $-COCH_3$)	5		1	1		7
171.9846	$C_8H_6Cl_2$	$Cl_2PhC_2H_3$‡X_2	1		1	2		4
		P.I.D. ions	7	3	4	3	7	24
		Other unclassified		1	3			4

m/e	Formula	Structural Significance	1	2	3	4	5	Total
172.9924	$C_8H_7Cl_2$	CH_3 (Cl_2) $PhCH_2$-, Cl_2PhCH (CH_3)-; $Cl_2PhCH_2CH_2$ ⫲ X	8		1	1		10
	Also:	Cl_2PhCO-, $C_{13}H_{17}$, $CHBrBr^{81}$, $C_2H_5COOCH_2CH$ $(OCOC_2H_5)$-	5			2	1	8
		P.I.D. ions	1	3		5	1	10
		Other unclassified	1	3	2	3	1	10
174.		CH_2=CH-CH_2N $(COCH_3)$ Ph ⫲ Cl, $HBrBr^{81}$ C ⫲ $COOC_2H_4$ ⫲ H (rearr.)?	1	1				2
		P.I.D. ions	7	11	4	5	3	30
		Other unclassified	1	1	1	2	1	6
174.9717	$C_7H_5OCl_2$	$Cl_2PhCHOH$ ⫲, $Cl_2(HO)PhCH_2$ ⫲, $Cl_2(HO)(CH_3)Ph$ ⫲ X $ClPhOCH_2$ ⫲ COOR, etc.	6	2	4			12
175.1486	$C_{13}H_{19}$	See $C_{10}H_{13}$ (*m/e* 133), also perhydropyrene	6	1	3	2		12
	Also:	$C_4Cl_2F_3$, $PhSiCl_2$-, H_2C=$CClCH_2OCOC_2H_4CO$-, $C_{12}H_{15}O$	2	1		2		5
		P.I.D. ions		15	3			18
		Other unclassified			3	1		4
176.1201	$C_{12}H_{16}O$	Cyclohexyl-PhO ⫲ R ⫲ H (rearr.),etc.		2	2			4
		P.I.D. ions	5	10	10	4		29
		Other unclassified		1	1	1		3

(Columns 1–5 are Relative Probability.)

m/e	Formula	Structural Significance	Relative Probability 1	2	3	4	5	Total
177.1279	$C_{12}H_{17}O$	C_4H_9 (HO) PhCH (CH_3) ‡, C_4H_9 (CH_3O) $PhCH_2$ ‡, etc. (see *m/e* 107)	6	1		4		11
	Also:	$C_2H_2Br^{81}$ Cl_2, $C_2H_5OCOPhCO$-, $C_6H_{10}OBr$, CF_2I	4	1	1	3		9
		P.I.D. ions		3	6	4		13
		Other unclassified	2	2	2	1		7
178.0782	$C_{14}H_{10}$	Dihydroethanoanthracene, etc.; Ph_2C_2 ‡ X_4; 179 larger	2	1	2	2		7
	Also:	$C_3Cl_3Cl^{37}$, HOPhN$(C_4H_9)CH_2$ ‡, PhCH(CH_3)N(C_2H_4OH) CH_2 ‡	2		2			4
		P.I.D. ions	4	10	7	1		22
		Other unclassified		1		2		3
178.9034	$C_3Cl_3F_2$		5		2	1		8
179.0860	$C_{14}H_{11}$	Ph_2C_2H ‡ Y (Y= X, H; HX_2), $(CH_3)_2PhOPO$ $(OPhCH_3)$ OR (rearr.), etc.	1	3	3	1		8
	Also:	C_2BrF_4, $CH_3OCOC_3H_5Br$ ‡, $C_2HBr^{81}ClF_2$, $C_3HCl_3Cl^{37}$, $C_{11}H_{15}O_2$, Cl_3Ph ‡ X	3		3	3		9
		P.I.D. ions	2	7	3	3		15
		Other unclassified	1			1		2
180.0660	$C_9H_{10}NO_3$	O_2N (HO) PhC $(CH_3)_2$-	2					2
180.0938	$C_{14}H_{12}$	$(CH_3PhCH_2\text{-})_2$, $(H_5C_2Ph\text{-})_2$, $(CH_3Ph\text{-})_2CHR$, $(PhCH)_2$ ‡ X_2			2		3	5
		P.I.D. ions	6	5	5	1	2	19
		Other unclassified				1	1	2

m/e	Formula	Structural Significance	Relative Probability 1	2	3	4	5	Total
180.9888	C_4F_7		1	3	2	1		7
	Also:	PhPhCH (CH_3) +, Cl (C_3H_7) PhCH (CH_3) +, PhPhNO + O	2	1	1			4
		P.I.D. ions	1	8	2	3		14
		Other unclassified	1			3		4
182.		Ph_2NCH_2 +, $(O_2N)_2PhNH$ + COR, $PhCH_2PhNH$ +		2		1	2	5
		P.I.D. ions	2	11	1	4	4	22
		Other unclassified	1		1			2
182.9446	C_7H_4BrO	BrPhCO +	4	1	1	1		7
182.9810	C_8H_8Br	See C_8H_9	3	4	1	2		10
183.0809	$C_{13}H_{11}O$	$PhOPhCH_2$ +, CH_3OPhPh + X, $PhCH_2PhO$ +, $PhPhOCH_2$ +, etc.	5	3	2	3		13
	Also:	Ph_2SiH-, CF_3SSCF_2 -			1	1		2
		P.I.D. ions	1	4		6		11
		Other unclassified	1		1	1		3
184.		$PhCH_2PhO$ + R + H (rearr.), $C_{12}H_{26}N$ (see *m/e* 170), $(O_2N)_2PhO$ + R + H (rearr.), H_2NPhBr + X, O + $ONPhCOCH_2$ + Br	3	2		2		7
		P.I.D. ions	4	10	10	6		30
		Other unclassified			1			1

m/e	Formula	Structural Significance	Relative Probability 1	2	3	4	5	Total
185.	$C_4H_9OOCC_4H_8CO$ ‡ OR, $C_2Cl_3Cl^{37}F$, X ‡ $ClPhOCH_2COO$ ‡ R ‡ H,(rearr.) C_3ClF_6, C_2HBrBr^{81} , Br (HO) (CH_3) Ph ‡ X		2	2	3		1	8
		P.I.D. ions	1	7	3	1	2	14
		Other unclassified		3		1	1	5
186.	PhOPhO ‡ R ‡ H (rearr.), $C_4H_9OOCC_4H_8CO$ ‡ OR ‡ H (rearr.), $C_2H_2BrBr^{81}$ ‡ Br_2, ClPhPh ‡ Cl_2		1	1	2			4
		P.I.D. ions	8		8	1	5	22
187.	$C_{14}H_{19}$ (see $C_{10}H_{11}$), $Cl_2PhC(CH_3)_2$-, $C_2H_3BrBr^{81}$		4		1	1	2	8
		P.I.D. ions	1	1	2	4	3	11
		Other unclassified	3	3				6
188.	In 10 highest peaks, only ion classified was $(n\text{-}C_4H_9O)_2BOCH_2$ ‡ R ‡ H (rearr.) (10th highest in spectrum)							
		P.I.D. ions	2	2	6	5	6	21
		Other unclassified				1		1
189.1642	$C_{14}H_{21}$	See $C_{10}H_{13}$ (m/e 133)	7	1		1		9
	Also: $C_8H_7OCl_2$ (see $C_7H_5OCl_2$), $C_{13}H_{17}O$, CH_2=$CHCH_2OCOPhCO$-		1	2	2			5
		P.I.D. ions	1	6	4			11
		Other unclassified			2	1		3

m/e	Formula	Structural Significance	1	2	3	4	5	6	7	Total
190.		Cl (O_2N) Ph ‡ Cl, 2-cyano-fluorene ‡ H	2	1						3
		P.I.D. ions	2	7	5	7				21
		Other unclassified				1				1
191.0860	$C_{15}H_{11}$, $C_{14}H_{23}$:	Anthracene-CH_2 ‡, phenanthrene-CH_2 ‡; tetradecahydroan-thracene ‡ etc.	6	3						9
191.1435	$C_{13}H_{19}O$	See *m/e* 177	3	3	3	1				10
	Also:	$C_4Cl_3F_2$, $C_3H_6ClOSiCl_2$-, C_3BrF_4, $CBrBr^{81}F$, $C_4HCl_3Cl^{37}$, $C_3H_4Br^{81}Cl_2$, C_4ClF_4S, $Br^{81}ClPh$ ‡ X, $C_2H_2F_2I$, $C_3H_7OCOPhCO$ ‡	8	2	1	6				17
		P.I.D. ions	2	2	3	1				8
192.		$CH_3OPhN(C_4H_9)CH_2$ ‡, Cl_2PhCCl ‡ Cl_2	1		1					2
		P.I.D. ions	5	2	7	4	2			20
		Other unclassified		1		1				2
193.	$C_{15}H_{13}$	(see *m/e* 179), (Cl_3PhC_1 -) (see *m/e* 159), $(C_2H_5O)_3SiOCH_2$ ‡, $C_{12}H_{17}O_2$ (see *m/e* 151), $SbCl_2$, $C_2H_5OCOC_3H_5Br$ ‡	7	3	2		1			13
		P.I.D. ions		6	3	2	1	3		15
		Other unclassified		1			2	1		4
194.	$C_4Cl_2F_4$,	$C_2H_5OCOPhCOO$ ‡ R ‡ H (rearr.), $Cl_3Ph(OH)$ ‡ HCl	2			1	1		1	5

m/e	Formula	Structural Significance	1	2	3	4	5	6	7	Total
194.	$C_4Cl_2F_4$	(Cont'd.)								
		P.I.D. ions	1	3	4	5	4	3	3	23
		Other unclassified			1			1	1	3
195.	$C_{15}H_{15}$	(see $C_{13}H_{11}$), Cl_3PhO-, $C_{14}H_{11}O$ [PhCOPh (CH_3)-, etc.], $(CH_3)_2PhOPO(OPhCH_3)$-OR, $C_{12}H_{16}Cl$ (see C_7H_6Cl), CF_3PhCF_2-, $PhBrC_3H_3$-	7	4	2	2	3	1	2	21
		P.I.D. ions	1	5	3	1		1		11
		Other unclassified	4	1	1				1	7
195.9249	$C_6H_3OCl_3$	See $C_6H_4OCl_2$ (*m/e* 162)	17	6	1	1				25
	Also:	$PhCH_2N(Ph)CH_2$-, C_9H_9Br (see C_9H_{10}), $(O_2N)_2Ph\ HCH_2$-			1	1	3			5
		P.I.D. ions	7	3	3	6	1			20
		Other unclassified		1		1	2			4
197.	$C_9H_{10}Br$	(see C_9H_{11}), $C_2Br^{81}ClF_3$, HOPhCOPh-, $HO(O_2N)_2$-$PhCH_2$-, $C_{14}H_{13}O$ (see $C_{13}H_{11}O$), C_4ClF_6, $H_9C_4(Cl)PhOCH_2$-, $BrCOC_2H_3Br^{81}$-, Ph_2Si-(CH_3)-, $C_{15}H_{17}$	8	7		3	4			22
		P.I.D. ions		1	5	1	1			8
		Other unclassified				2				2
198.		$(H_{13}C_6)_2NCH_2$-, $HO(O_2N)_2PhCH_2$-, $(CH_3)_2NCONHPhCl \nmid X$	1	1	1					3
		P.I.D. ions	2	26	12	9				49
		Other unclassified	1							1

m/e	Formula	Structural Significance	1	2	3	4	5	6	7	Total
199.	$C_3H_3BrBr^{81}$, Br (HO PhCO ┼ R, Cl_2-benzofuran-CH_2 ┼ R, $C_3HCl_3F_3$		2	2			1			5
		P.I.D. ions		4	5	3	3	5		20
		Other unclassified		2						2
200.	ClPhC (Ph)╪HCl (?) RCOO ┼ $C_3H_4Br_2$ ┼ H		1			1				2
		P.I.D. ions	4	3	13	9	6			35
		Other unclassified	1			2	2			5
201.	$C_3H_5BrBr^{81}$, $C_2HOBrBr^{81}$, ClPhCH_2Ph ┼ X, $C_3Cl_2F_5$, $C_2Cl_4Cl^{37}$, $(C_4H_9)_2(CH_3)_2Si_2H$-, $C_{16}H_9$		4		2	1	1	2		10
		P.I.D. ions	1	1	3	3	3	2	2	15
		Other unclassified	1		1	1			1	4
202.	Hg, Hg ╪ $(CF_3)_2$, (ClPhOPh) ╪ Cl_2, Cl_2 (CH_3O) Ph-CHCH_2 ┼ C_4H_8		2	1	1	1				5
		P.I.D. ions	5	4	3	4	4	1		21
203.0030	$C_9H_9OCl_2$	See $C_7H_5OCl_2$	1			1			1	3
203.0263	$C_{12}H_8OCl$	ClPhOPh ┼ X, ClPhPh (OH) ┼ X, Cl (PhPh) O ┼ COR			1		2	1	1	5
203.1799	$C_{15}H_{23}$	See $C_{10}H_{15}$, (*m/e* 133)	2	3	1	1				7
		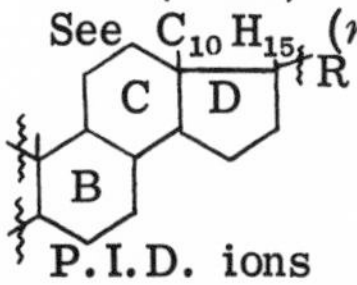 (?)						2	2	4
		P.I.D. ions		2	5	2	3	2	2	16
		Other unclassified	1					2		3

m/e	Formula	Structural Significance	1	2	3	4	5	6	7	Total
204.		Phenanthrene = $(CH_2)_2$ ╪ (CH_2CH_2), $C_4H_5Br^{81}Cl_2$		1	1					2
		P.I.D. ions	5	6	5	4	2	4	1	27
		Other unclassified				1		1	1	3
205.		$C_{14}H_{21}O$ (see *m/e* 177), sesquiterpenones, $C_7H_5Br^{81}Cl$, $C_4H_9OCOPhCO$┼, C_6F_7, $C_2H_5OC_6H_9Br$┼X, $BrPhCF_2$┼, Br-naphthyl┼X,	7	1	1			3	1	13
		P.I.D. ions	1	1	3		3	3	3	14
		Other unclassified		1		3				4
206.		$C_4H_9(C_3H_5O)PhO$┼R┼H (rearr.), C_2PhCl_3╪Cl_2		1	1	2				4
		P.I.D. ions	7	9	6	2	3			27
		Other unclassified			1		1			2
207.		$C_{13}H_{19}O_2$, $C_{12}H_{15}O_3$ (see *m/e* 151), Cl_3PhC_2┼ (see *m/e* 173), methylsiloxanes, $CBrBr^{81}Cl$, $C_{16}H_{15}$	8	4	1	1	2			16
		P.I.D. ions	1	4		3	6			14
		Other unclassified	1	1		1				3
207.9766	Pb	R_4Pb		3	7					10
	Also:	$OCNPhCH_2Ph$┼, $PhPhOC_3H_3$╪C_3HPh		1	1					2
		P.I.D. ions	7	9	8	4				28
		Other unclassified		2	1					3

m/e	Formula	Structural Significance	1	2	3	4	5	6	7	Total
209.	$C_{13}H_{18}Cl$ (see C_7H_6Cl), $C_{12}H_{14}ClO$, $C_4Cl_3Cl^{37}F$, $C_{15}H_{13}O$, CH_3 (PhCOPh) CH_2‡ (see *m/e* 195), $C_7H_4Cl_3O$ (see C_7H_7O), $C_3Br^{81}ClF_3$, Bi‡R_3, $H_7C_3OOCPhCOO$‡-R‡H (rearr.)		7	4	3		1	3		18
		P.I.D. ions		5	4	1	3	1		14
		Other unclassified				2	1			3
210.	$O_2NPhCH{=}CClCO$‡				1					1
		P.I.D. ions	6	8	4	6	5	2		31
		Other unclassified			1					1
211.1122	$C_{15}H_{15}O$	HOPhPhC $(CH_3)_2$‡, PhOPhC $(CH_3)_2$‡, etc.	7	1						8
	Also: HO$(O_2N)_2$PhCH(CH_3)‡, C_3HBrF_5, $(H_9C_4O)_2$OPO-‡R‡H_2 (rearr.), $C_2HBr^{81}Cl_3$, $C_4HCl_3F_3$, PhPhSi$(CH_3)_2$‡, $H_{11}C_5$-naphthyl-CH_2‡		8		6				1	15
		P.I.D. ions	1	5	5	4	1	4	2	22
212.	H_5C_3(Br)PhO‡COR‡H (rearr.), PhOPhC_3H_6‡R‡H (rearr.)		2	1			1			4
		P.I.D. ions	2	4	7	8	6	3		30
		Other unclassified	1		1					2

m/e	Formula	Structural Significance	1	2	3	4	5	6	7	8	9	10	Total
213.	$C_4Cl_2F_5$, HO (Br) PhC $(CH_3)_2 \dagger$, $C_3Cl_4Cl^{37}$, $C_2Br^{81}Cl_2F_2$, $C_4H_5BrBr^{81}$, $(CF_3)_2Ph \dagger$, Ph_2Cl (C=C) $\dagger$X, 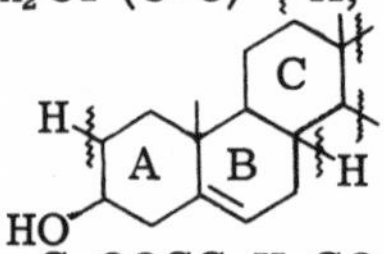 (?), $H_{13}C_6OOCC_4H_8CO \dagger$, etc.		6	2	2	1	2	3	4				20
		P.I.D. ions		5	1	6		3	1				16
		Other unclassified				1							1
214.		P.I.D. ions	3	10	5	3	2	3	4				30
215.1799	$C_{16}H_{23}$	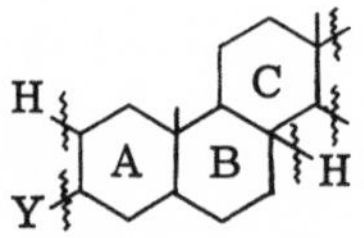 (?) (Y= OH, -OCOR), corresp. olefin	1	2	3	1		3	2				12
	Also: $C_4H_7BrBr^{81}$, $(H_5C_2)_2Cl_2PhCH_2 \dagger$, $Cl_3Cl^{81}Ph \dagger$, CH_3-benzanthracene		2				1		1				4
		P.I.D. ions		2	2	2	2		1				9
216.		P.I.D. ions	7	3		2	8	1	2				23
		Other unclassified					1						1
217.1955	$C_{16}H_{25}$	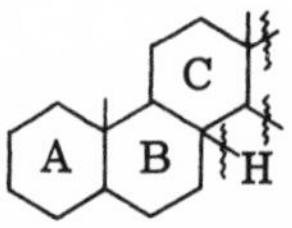 (?)	2	2	1		1						6

m/e	Formula	Structural Significance	1	2	3	4	5	6	7	8	9	10	Total
217.1955	$C_{16}H_{25}$	(Cont'd.)											
	Also:	Other $C_{16}H_{25}$ (see $C_{10}H_{13}$), $CH_3O(Cl_2)PhC(CH_3)_2$+, Cl (CH_3O) PhPh+Cl, CH_3Hg+, $(PhO)_2P$+, $C_3Cl_3F_4$	4	1	1				1				7
		P.I.D. ions			2	1	2	2	1				8
218.	HOPhI ǂ I_2, $(H_9C_4)_2NCHPh$ +			1	1								2
		P.I.D. Ions	5	3	7	3	4	1	2				25
219.	$C_2BrBr^{81}Cl$, C_4F_9, Cl+Cl_2	$PhOCH_2COO$+R+H (rearr.), $BrPhSO_2$-; $C_8H_7Br^{81}Cl$ (see C_8H_9)			2	1	1	1	2	2			9
		P.I.D. ions		1	1	3		2	1		2	1	11
220.	ClPhOPhO ǂ R ǂ H (rearr.),	$(CH_3)_2NCOPh(C_4H_9)$ ǂ Cl; H_9C_4 (C_6H_{11})-cyclohexyl- ǂ HOH	1	1					1				3
		P.I.D. ions	3	3	4		3	2	5	2	1	1	24
		Other unclassified		1		1	1						3
221.	$C_6H_{17}O_3Si_3$, Ph_2-C_5H_7+R,	Cl_2Ph_2+, $(H_3COOC)_2Ph$-CO+, C_4ClF_6, $Cl_2(CH_3O)_2$-PhO+, $Cl_3(H_5C_2)PhCH_2$+, PhCOCH=C (Ph) CH_2+, OC+NPhCH(-NCO)+(?), Cl_3-2, 3-dihydrobenzo-furyl+; Cl_2PhOCH_2COO-ǂ R ǂ H, $C_2H_2BrBr^{81}Cl$	3	3	4	3	1		1	1	1	1	18
		P.I.D. ions	1	1	1	5	5		1	1	2	1	18
		Other unclassified		2	1	1					1	1	6

m/e	Formula	Structural Significance	1	2	3	4	5	6	7	8	9	10	Total
			Relative Probability										
222.	C_4BrF_5 ; $C_5Cl_3F_3$				1				1				2
		P.I.D. ions	4	2	7	3	3	2	6	5	4	1	37
		Other unclassified									2		2
223.0001	CH_3Pb	CH_3Pb ǂ RR'R"	3	5	1								9
	Also:	$C_3H_7Ph_2CH(CH_3)$ ǂ, $Cl(H_7C_3)_2PhCH(CH_3)$ ǂ, etc., $H_9C_4(O_2N)_2Ph$ ǂ, $H_9C_4OOCPhCOO$ ǂ R ǂ H_2 (rearr.), $C_4ClF_4S_2$, H ǂ R ǂ $Ph_2(C_3H_7)CH(CH_3)$ ǂ (rearr.), Cl_3PhOCH-(CH_3) ǂ COOR; $H_{21}C_{10}$–cyclohexyl ǂ	3		4	1	1	1		1			11
		P.I.D. ions		2	2	4	1	1			2	5	17
		Other unclassified					1				1		2
224.	H ǂ $H_{30}C_{15}(H_{11}C_5)CH$ ǂ R, H_9C_4OPhPh ǂ HCl, (C_6F_8)								1		1		2
		P.I.D. ions	3	6		4	6	2	1	3		1	26
		Other unclassified									1	1	2
225.	$Cl(H_9C_4)(HO)PhC(CH_3)_2$ ǂ, etc. $C_4Cl_4Cl^{37}$, $C_3Br^{81}Cl_2F_2$, $H_{11}C_5$-naphthyl-$CH(CH_3)$ ǂ, $HO(O_2N)_2PhC(CH_3)_2$ ǂ, $Br(H_7C_3)PhCH(CH_3)$ ǂ, PhOOCPhCO ǂ OR, $PhOPhC_4H_8$ ǂ ; $C_5Cl_2F_5$, $H_{31}C_{15}(H_{11}C_5)CH$ ǂ R		6	1	2	1					1	2	13
		P.I.D. ions		2		1		2		2	1	4	12
		Other unclassified	1		1	1	1			1		1	6

m/e	Formula	Structural Significance	1	2	3	4	5	6	7	8	9	10	Total
226.	$(H_{15}C_7)_2NCH_2$ †, etc.,												
	$C_{18}H_{10}$ ‡ (H) R,												
	$PhPhOC_3H_4(OH)$ ‡ HOH;		1	3	3	2	1	3	1				14
		P.I.D. ions	3	6	2	2	4	4	2	3	1	2	29
		Other unclassified			1						1		2
227.	$C_{18}H_{11}$ † R, $H_9C_4(HO)PhBr$ † X				1		1	1		2		1	6
		P.I.D. ions		9	3	1	2	1	2	4	2	2	26
		Other unclassified		1			1						2
228.	$C_{18}H_{12}$ ‡ (H) R etc.;												
	$C_5H_8BrBr^{81}$ ‡ HBr					2	1	1					4
		P.I.D. ions	4	3	3	2	4	1	2	1	1	1	22
229.	$Cl_3Cl^{37}(H_3C)Ph$ † X, etc.,												
	$C_5H_9BrBr^{81}$ † X,												
	$C_3HBr^{81}ClF_4$,												
	$BrHC{=}CBr^{81}C(OH)$-												
	(CH_3) † R, $C_{11}H_{13}Si_3$,												
	Cl_3PhO † C_2HCl † Cl^{37}												
	(rearr.), $C_4HCl_3Cl^{37}F_2$,												
	$C_4Cl_3F_4$, PhPhPh † R;												
	$F_3CCClFC(CF_3)(OCH_3)$-												
	† OR		9			2	2	2	1	1	1	2	20
		P.I.D. ions		1	3	1	2	1	1			2	11
		Other unclassified						1					1
230.	$H_{13}C_6CON(Ph)C_3H_4$ † X		1										1
		P.I.D. ions	2	4			2	2	1	1	3	1	16
		Other unclassified	1										1

m/e	Formula	Structural Significance	1	2	3	4	5	6	7	8	9	10	Total
231.	$(H_9C_4)_2PhC(CH_3)_2$‡, etc., $ClH_4C_2OPh(Cl)C(CH_3)_2$‡, $H_{21}C_{10}CHPh$‡, perhydrobenzanthracene‡R, $ClH_4C_3OOCC_2H_4$- $COOC_3H_4$‡X, H_5C_2Hg‡R, C_5F_9; CH_2ICHPh‡OH, $Cl_3Cl^{37}(HO)Ph$‡X		2	1	3	2		4	1	2	1	1	17
		P.I.D. ions		1	4	2	3	2	1				13
		Other unclassified	1					1			1		3
232.		P.I.D. ions	6	1	1	2	1	2	2	1		3	19
233.	$C_{16}H_{25}O$ [$C_{16}H_{23}$ (see *m/e* 215) $+H_2O$], Cl_3-benzo- furan-CH_2‡, $(C_2H_4ClO)_2POC_2H_4$‡Cl, BrPhPh‡X; C_7ClF_6, $(PhO)_2PO$‡OPh			1		2	2	1			1		7
		P.I.D. ions		2		1		3	1	2	1	4	14
		Other unclassified			1								1
234.	$BrBr^{81}Ph$‡Br_2							1					1
		P.I.D. ions	1	4	4	1	4	3	4				21
		Other unclassified					1	1					2
235.	$(ClPh)_2CH$‡Y (Y= X, R), $C_3Cl_3Cl^{37}F_3$, Br_2Ph‡Y*, $C_3H_6ClOSiCl_2$- OC_2H_4‡, $(C_6H_{11}CH_2CH_2)_2CH$‡R; $(C_2H_5)_2Cl_3Ph$‡Cl		5	1	2	2	1	1	3	4		1	20
		P.I.D. ions		2	3	1	3	1		1		1	12
		Other unclassified							1				1

m/e	Formula	Structural Significance	1	2	3	4	5	6	7	8	9	10	Total
236.	$HO(O_2N)Ph(C_7H_{14})$+, $PhOPhCl_2$‡Cl_2, CH_2=$CHSPh(Cl_3)$‡Cl_2, $Cl_3(C_3H_5)PhO$+COR+H (rearr.); H_9C_5-$C_{12}H_{23}$‡(H) R, $Br_2(H_3C)(HO)Ph$‡Br_2, (C_7F_8)		3	1							3		7
	P.I.D. ions		8	3	1	6	2	1	2	2		1	26
	Other unclassified				1		1	1	1		1		5
237.	H_5C_2Pb‡R_3, $H_{17}C_8$-thiophene - $C(CH_3)_2$+, $Cl(H_7C_3)_2(CH_3)$-$PhCH(CH_3)$+, etc., $PhOPhCl_2$+Cl		3	2		2	1	2	3		1	1	15
	P.I.D. ions		1	2	1	3	1	3	2	2	2	4	21
	Other unclassified						1				1	4	6
238.	$(CH_3)_2Pb$‡R_2											2	2
	P.I.D. ions		7	5	5	4		5	1	1	3	4	35
	Other unclassified						1					1	2
239.	$Br^{81}Cl_3PhCH_2$+, $H_{11}C_5$-naphthyl-C_3H_6+, $PhSiH_2PhSi(CH_3)_2$+, $C_{19}H_{11}$ (*m/e* 241 larger), $H_{35}C_{17}$+COOR, $C_4H_5Br^{81}Cl_3$+; $PhOPhC_5H_{10}$+, $C_{15}H_{31}CO$+		1	2	5	2			1		1	1	13
	P.I.D. ions			2	1	2			1	1	2	2	11
	Other unclassified			1				1					2
240.	$C_5Cl_3Cl^{37}F_2$, $C_{19}H_{12}$ (*m/e* 239 larger); $Cl_3PhOCH_2CH_2O$-+R+H (rearr.)					2	1	1	1		2		7
	P.I.D. ions		1	5	2	5	7	1	1	3	1		26

m/e	Formula	Structural Significance	1	2	3	4	5	6	7	8	9	10	Total
241.	$BrBr^{81}$-cyclohexyl +, C_4BrF_6, $C_5Cl_3F_4$, $ClC_2H_4OC_2H_4OPhC$-$(CH_3)_2$ +, $C_{19}H_{13}$ (benzophenanthrene-CH_2+, etc.); $Br^{81}Cl_2(HO)Ph$+X, $H_9C_4OOCC_8H_{16}CO$+, $C_5HCl_3Cl^{37}F_2$, CHBr=CBrC (OH)-(C_2H_5)+		4	4	1		1	1	2			3	16
		P.I.D. ions		3	1	2		2	2		2		12
242.	Ph=$(C_2Cl_3Cl^{37})$+Cl_2, etc., $C_5HCl_3F_4$;			1		2		2	1				6
		P.I.D. ions	4		3	2	3	2	3	6	4	1	28
243.	$Cl_2(H_5C_2)_3PhCH_2$+, etc., $HCl_2CPhCClCl^{37}$+, etc., Ph_3C+, Cl_3PhSO_2+; C_6F_9		4	1	1		1			2	2	1	12
		P.I.D. ions		3	2	1		1					7
		Other unclassified			1		2		1				4
244.	Ph_2NPh+H (245 base)			1									1
		P.I.D. ions	3	3	2	4	3	2	1	1			19
		Other unclassified					1					1	2
245.	Tetrahydronaphthacene-CH_2+, perhydronaphthacene-+R, $(CF_3CH_2O)_2PO$-+OR; $H_5C_3O(H_9C_4)_2Ph$-+Cl			2		1					1		4
		P.I.D. ions	1	1	4	2	4	1	1	2			16
		Other unclassified				1							1

m/e	Formula	Structural Significance	1	2	3	4	5	6	7	8	9	10	Total
246.		P.I.D. ions		4	4	2	1	4	2	4	3		24
		Other unclassified		2									2
247.	$Cl_3Cl^{37}(HO)PhO$ † CH_3, C_5ClF_8, $C_4Cl_3Cl^{37}F_3$		1		2			1					4
		P.I.D. ions			2			1	1	4	2	2	12
		Other unclassified			1					1			2
248.	$(H_5C_2)_4$-cyclo-Si_3O_3 ‡ $(C_2H_5)_2$(?), $Ph_2Cl_2C_2$- ‡ Cl_2			1		1							2
		P.I.D. ions	1	3	3		2		1	2	1	4	17
249.	$Cl_3(H_5C_2)_2PhCH_2$ †, etc., $BrBr^{81}PhCH_2$ †, etc., $(C_3H_6ClO)_2SiCl$ †, $Cl_4Cl^{37}Ph$ †, other, $C_6Cl_4Cl^{37}$, $C_3HCl_5Cl^{37}$, $(ClH_4C_2O)_2POOC_2H_4$- † Cl, $C_7Cl_2F_5$; $(OCNPh)_2CH$ †		4	1	2	6	1	3		1	1		19
		P.I.D. ions		1	1	2			1	1	1	1	8
250.	$BrBr^{81}(H_2N)Ph$ † Br						1						1
		P.I.D. ions	5	3		5	3			1	2	2	21
		Other unclassified				2						1	3

m/e	Formula	Structural Significance	1	2	3	4	5	6	7	8	9	10	Total
251.	CBr_2Br^{81},	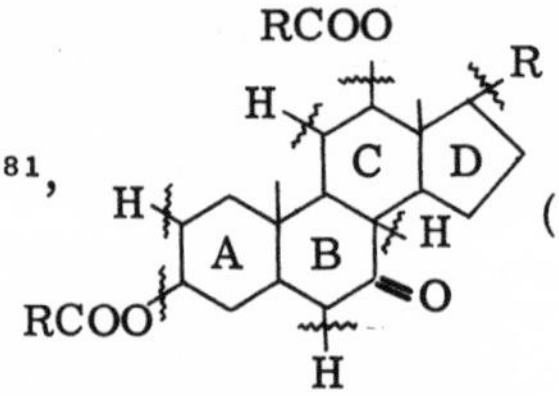 (?), $Cl(H_9C_4)_2PhCH(CH_3)$ +, $PhPhC(CH_3)_2CH_2C$-$(CH_3)_2$ +, $C_3Cl_4Cl^{37}F_2$; $BrBr^{81}(HO)Ph$ + Br, $C_6H_{11}CH_2CH(C_{10}H_{21})$ +	2	1		2			2				7
		P.I.D. ions		4	1	5	3	4	2	1	4	1	25
		Other unclassified							1				1
252.		P.I.D. ions	3	3	3	2	3	4	3	2	2	2	27
		Other unclassified			1					1			2
253.	$(CH_3)_3Pb$,	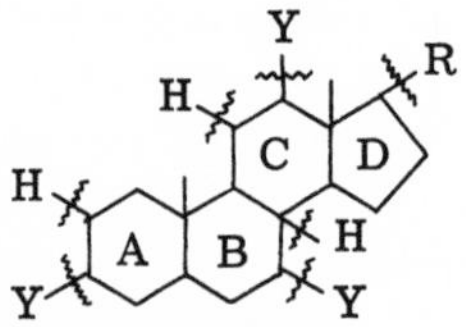 (?), (Y= -OH, -COOR), corresp. olefins $(C_{19}H_{25})$, $Cl_2PhC_2H_3Br^{81}$ + Br	6	3	3		1						13
		P.I.D. ions			3	1	1	1	1				7
		Other unclassified		1				1					2
254.	I_2 + CHI,	I_2 + CH_2 (rearrs.)	1			1							2
		P.I.D. ions	4	3	5	2	1			1			16
		Other unclassified					1				2		3

m/e	Formula	Structural Significance	1	2	3	4	5	6	7	8	9	10	Total
255.	$C_2HBrBr^{81}Cl_2$, $C_{19}H_{27}$ ($C_{19}H_{25}$ less one Y gp.), C_7F_9; CH_3-benzanthracene-CH_2 ⨦		1				3		2		1	1	8
		P.I.D. ions						1					1
256.	$C_6Cl_2F_6$								1				1
		P.I.D. ions	3	1	1	3		2	2		1	2	15
		Other unclassified										1	1
257.	$C_{19}H_{29}$ ($C_{19}H_{25}$ less 2 Y gps.), Cl_3Cl^{37} (H_5C_2) $PhCH_2$ ⨦		4	1			1	1	2		2		11
		P.I.D. ions		4			1						5
		Other unclassified	1										1
258.		P.I.D. ions	4	3		1	1	1	1	3	3	1	18
		Other unclassified									1		1
259.	$C_6H_5Cl_5Cl^{37}$ ⨦ Cl, $C_5Cl_3Cl^{37}F_3$, $C_4H_3Br^{81}Cl_2F_3$, $(CH_3)_2PhCH$ ($C_{11}H_{21}$) ⨦, etc., C_4H_8ClOPh (Cl) C-$(CH_3)_2$ ⨦		3	1	1	1					1		7
		P.I.D. ions				3				1	1		5
		Other unclassified		1									1
260.	$C_4Cl_5Cl^{37}$				1								1
		P.I.D. ions		2	2	1	4	2	1	2			14

(Columns 1–10 under "Relative Probability")

m/e	Formula	Structural Significance	1	2	3	4	5	6	7	8	9	10	Total
			Relative Probability										
261.	$C_4Cl_3F_4S$, $C_5HCl_3F_5$		1			1						1	3
		P.I.D. ions	1	3	3		1	1	2	1	1		13
		Other unclassified							1				1
262.	H ǂ ($BrBr^{81}$) PhCO ǂ OH, (C_6F_{10})										1		1
		P.I.D. ions	4	1		5	2	2	2	2		1	19
263.	Cl_4Cl^{37} $PhCH_2$ ǂ, $BrBr^{81}$ PhCH (CH_3) ǂ, $C_2Br_2Br^{81}$		3		1	3	2						9
		P.I.D. ions	1	2	1	1	2				1		8
264.	$C_2HBr_2Br^{81}$, H ǂ cyclohexyl-(CH_3) - CH ($C_{11}H_{23}$) ǂ R					2							2
		P.I.D. ions	3	2	5		2	1	1			1	15
265.	$C_2H_2Br_2Br^{81}$, $(H_7C_3)_2$PhPhCH (CH_3) ǂ, etc., $H_{33}C_{17}CO$ ǂ, $H_{13}C_7CH$ ($C_{11}H_{23}$) ǂ		1	1		1					2	1	6
		P.I.D. ions	1	1	2	1	4		2	1		4	16
266.	Cl_4Cl^{37} PhO ǂ R ǂ H (rearr.), $(F_3C)_2$-triazine-CF_2 ǂ; I_2C ǂ H_2		1				1					1	3
		P.I.D. ions	2	1	1	1	5	3	1	2			16

m/e	Formula / Structural Significance	1	2	3	4	5	6	7	8	9	10	P.I.D.	Uncl.	Total
267.	(H_9C_4) PhOPhC $(CH_3)_2$ †, C_3H_6ClOPh (C_4H_9) C-$(CH_3)_2$ †, H_5C_2 $(H_3C)_2$ Pb‡, I_2CH†, $H_{35}C_{17}$CO‡; $C_4Cl_3F_6$, (naphthyl)$_2$-CH†	3			1	1	1	1		3				10
	P.I.D. ions		1	1			2	1	3	1	2			11
	Other unclassified					1								1
268.	$(H_{17}C_8)_2$NCO‡, (C_8F_9)			1										1
	P.I.D. ions	2	2	4	1	1	3	1	2					16
	Other unclassified							1						1
269.	$C_6H_4BrF_6$, $C_{19}H_{25}O$ (*m/e* 251 steroid + HOH), BrBr^{81} ClPh†X; $C_{15}H_{21}Si_2$, C_5F_{11}	3				1		1			1			6
	P.I.D. ions		1			2				1	1			5
	Other unclassified									1				1
270.												11		11
271.	$C_{19}H_{27}O$ (*m/e* 255 steroid + =O), CF_3Hg‡; CF_3PhPhCF_2†, Cl_3 (PhOPh)†X	1		1			1				1	4	3	11
272.	$C_5Cl_5Cl^{37}$ ‡X_2						1	1				9		11
273.	$C_{19}H_{29}O$ (*m/e* 255 steroid + HOH), Br (F_3C) PhCF_2†; C_3HBrBr^{81} F_4		1	1							1	5		8

m/e	Structural Significance	1	2	3	4	5	6	7	8	9	10	P. I. D.	Uncl.	Total
		Relative Probability												
274.	(C_7F_{10})											13	1	14
275.	$C_5Cl_4Cl^{37}F_2$, H_9C_4-phenanthrene-C $(CH_3)_2$ †, $C_4Br^{81}Cl_2F_4$, $(CF_3CH_2O)_2POOCH_2$ †; $H_9C_4OOCCH_2O$- $PhCl_2$ † Cl	2	1			1				1	1	8		14
276.	$Cl^{37}PhC_2Cl_4$ ‡ Cl_2					2						12	1	15
277.	$Cl_2Cl^{37}CPhCCl_2$ †, etc., $(H_5C_2)_5$-cyclotrisiloxane † R, PhH_4C_3C (Ph) (CH_3) †; $BrBr^{81}$-dihydrobenzofuran †, $BrBr^{81}PhC(CH_3)_2$ †, dibenzanthracene † H	5				1			2	1		8	2	19
278.	H † C_6H_{10}-CH $(C_{13}H_{27})$ † R							1			1	14	2	18
279.	$C_3H_4Br_2Br^{81}$, naphthyl-CH $(C_{10}H_{19})$ †, $C_5HCl_3Cl^{37}F_4$	1			1	1	2					9	1	15
280.	$H_{21}C_{10}CH(C_9H_{18})$ ‡ (H) R									1		13		14

m/e	Structural Significance	1	2	3	4	5	6	7	8	9	10	P.I.D.	Uncl.	Total
							Relative Probability							
281.	$(H_3C)_7Si_4O_4$ ┼ R, $H_3C(H_5C_2)_2$-Pb ┼, $(H_7C_3)_3$(PhPh) ┼, $C_9H_5F_8O$; $H_{13}C_6$ PhOPhC_2H_4 ┼, $H_{21}C_{10}$CH (C_9H_{19}) ┼, Cl_4Cl^{37} PhS ┼, C_6F_{11}	2		1	1			1	1	1	3	10		20
282.												13	3	16
283.	BrBr^{81} PhCHCl ┼									1		3	2	6
284.	$C_6Cl_5Cl^{37}$	3										8		11
285.	Tetrahydronaphthyl-CH $(C_{10}H_{21})$ ┼, $C_8H_2F_9O$		1					1				3		5
286.	PhBi ╪ R_2, (C_8F_{10})				1							10	1	12
287.	$H_{29}C_{14}$ CHPh ┼			1								1	3	5
288.												6		6
289.												1	1	2
290.												5		5

m/e	Structural Significance	Relative Probability 1	2	3	4	5	6	7	8	9	10	P.I.D.	Uncl.	Total
291.	$C_5HBr^{81}ClF_6$, decahydronaphthyl - CH $(C_{10}H_{21})$ ┼		1								1	3	1	6
292.	$BrBr^{81}$ H_5C_3PhO ┼ COR ┼ H (rearr.)							1				10	1	12
293.	$BrBr^{81}(HO)PhC(CH_3)_2$ ┼ $C_4H_6Br_2Br^{81}$, C_7F_{11}; $(naphthyl)_2$-C=$CHCH_2$ ┼, $(ClH_6C_3O)_2SiClOC_2H_4$ ┼	1	1			1	1	1	1			4	1	11
294.	$BrBr^{81}$ H_5C_3PhO ┼ COR ┼ H (rearr.), H ┼ $(H_{20}C_{10})$-CH $(C_{10}H_{21})$ ┼ R				1					1		8		10
295.	$Cl_3PhOPSCl^{37}$ ┼, $H_{13}C_6PhOPhC_3H_6$ ┼, $(H_5C_2)_3Pb$ ┼, etc.; $(H_{21}C_{10})_2CH$ ┼, etc.	2	1		1		1	1			2	4		12
296.												7		7
297.	$C_5Cl_3Cl^{37}F_5$							1				3		4
298.												3	1	4
299.	H_9C_4-pyrene-C $(CH_3)_2$ ┼		1									2		3

m/e	Structural Significance	1	2	3	4	5	6	7	8	9	10	P.I.D.	Uncl.	Total
		Relative Probability												
300.												3	1	4
301.	$C_2HBrBr^{81}_2Cl$	1												1
302.												1	2	3
303.												1	1	2
304.	None													
305.	C_8F_{11}								1				1	2
306.												4		4
307.	$[H_3C(H_9C_4)Ph-]_2CH^{+\cdot}$ etc., $C_5Cl_6Cl^{37}$	1								1		1	1	4
308.												5	1	6
309.	$H_{35}C_{17}CH(C_4H_9)^{+\cdot}$, etc.								3		3	4	2	12
310.												5		5

m/e	Structural Significance	1	2	3	4	5	6	7	8	9	10	P. I. D.	Uncl.	Total
		Relative Probability												
311.	$Cl_3CPh(Cl)CClCl^{37}$ ┼	2										1		3
312.	(C_7F_{12})											6	1	7
313.	Br_2Br^{81} Ph ┼ X, $C_5Cl_4Cl^{37}F_4$								1		1	3		5
314.												5	1	6
315.	$C_3H_3BrBr_2^{81}Cl$	1										3		4
316.												2	2	4
317.	(C_9F_{11})											1		1
318.												2		2
319.	$C_6Cl_6Cl^{37}$, (C_6F_{13})			1										1
320.												1		1
321.												1		1

m/e	Structural Significance	1	2	3	4	5	6	7	8	9	10	P.I.D.	Uncl.	Total
322.												3		3
323.												1	1	2
324.	$(CF_3CH_2O)_2POOC_2HF_2 \ddagger HF$, (C_8F_{12})	1										2	1	4
325.	$[HO(C_4H_9)Ph-]_2C(CH_3)^{+}$, $(F_3CCH_2O)_2POOCH_2CF_2^{+}$	1	1											2
326.												2		2
327.	$(H_9C_4OOC)_2C_3H_3COOC_3H_6^{+}$, $Br_2Br^{81}PhCH_2^{+}$		1	1								1		3
328.												2		2
329.	$H_{35}C_{17}CH(Ph)^{+}$									1		2		3
330.												3		3
331.	$C_{21}H_{23}Si_2$, (C_7F_{13})	1										1		2
332.												1		1

m/e	Structural Significance	Relative Probability 1	2	3	4	5	6	7	8	9	10	P.I.D.	Uncl.	Total
333.												1		1
334.												2		2
335.	None													
336.	(C_9F_{12})											1		1
337.	$H_{43}C_{21}$ CH (C_2H_5) ╪							1						1
338.												2		2
339.												2		2
340.												2	1	3
341.	Br_2Br^{81} PhCH (CH_3) ╪	1										1		2
342.												8		8
343.	Br_2Br^{81} (HO) (H_3C) Ph ╪ Br; C_8F_{13}				1					1		3		5

m/e	Structural Significance	Relative Probability 1	2	3	4	5	6	7	8	9	10	P. I. D.	Uncl.	Total
344.	$C_2Br_2Br^{81}_2 \ddagger X_2$	2										4	1	7
345.	$C_2HBr_2Br^{81}_2 \dagger X$, I_2 (HO) Ph $\dagger$ X	2										2		4
346.												8		8
347.												3		3
348.	$(C_{10}F_{12})$											2		2
349.												1		1
350.												2	1	3
351.													1	1
352.												2		2
353.	None													
354.												1		1

m/e	Structural Significance	1	2	3	4	5	6	7	8	9	10	P.I.D.	Uncl.	Total
		Relative Probability												
355.	Silicones, (C_9F_{13})											2		2
356.												2		2
357.												1		1
358.												4		4
359.	$C_3H_3Br_2Br^{81}_2$ -	1												1
360.	None													
361.												1		1
362.	(C_8F_{14})													
363.	None													
364.												2	1	3
365.												2	1	3

m/e	Structural Significance	1	2	3	4	5	6	7	8	9	10	P.I.D.	Uncl.	Total
366.	None													
367.	(C_{10} F_{13})													
368.	Cholestene ╪ (H) OY (Y= -OH, -OCOR)	1	1										2	4
369.	(C_7F_{15})													
370.	Cholestane ╪ (H) OY (Y= -OH, -OCOR)	1		2		1						1		5
371.	None													
372.	None													
373.	None													
374.	(C_9F_{14})													
375.	None													
376.	None													

m/e	Structural Significance	1	2	3	4	5	6	7	8	9	10	P.I.D.	Uncl.	Total
377.	None													
378.	None													
379.	$(C_{11}F_{13})$												1	1
380.	None													
381.	C_8F_{15}						1			1				2
382.	None													
383.													1	1
384.	None													
385.	None													
386.	$(C_{10}F_{14})$												1	1
387.	None													

m/e	Structural Significance	Relative Probability 1	2	3	4	5	6	7	8	9	10	P.I.D.	Uncl.	Total
388.													1	1
389.	None													
390.												2		2
391.	None													
392.												1		1
393.	(C_9F_{15})													
394.												3		3
395.												1		1
396.												1		1
397.	None													
398.												1		1

m/e		1	2	3	4	5	6	7	8	9	10	P.I.D.	Uncl.	Total
399.	None													
Grand Total		4036	3926	3864	1728	883	387	184	119	107	112	349	51	15,746

m/e	Ion
400.*	
401.	$C_4 Br_2 Br^{81} F_6$ (6th peak)
402.	
403.	
404.	
405.	$C_{10} F_{15}$
406.	
407.	
408.	
409.	
410.	
411.	
412.	$C_9 F_{16}$
413.	
414.	
415.	
416.	
417.	$C_{11} F_{15}$

* Above *m/e* 400 there are only 20 P.I.D. and unclassified entries in the Dow punched card file.

m/e	Ion
418.	
419.	
420.	
421.	
422.	
423.	
424.	$C_{10}F_{16}$
425.	
426.	
427.	
428.	
429.	Silicones
430.	
431.	C_9F_{17}
432.	
433.	
434.	
435.	
436.	$C_{11}F_{16}$

m/e	Ion
437.	
438.	
439.	
440.	
441.	
442.	
443.	$C_{10}F_{17}$
444.	
445.	
446.	
447.	$C_4Br_3Br_2^{81}$ (1st peak)
448.	$C_{12}F_{16}$
449.	
450.	
451.	
452.	
453.	
454.	
455.	$C_{11}F_{17}$

m/e	Ion
456.	
457.	
458.	
459.	
460.	
461.	
462.	$C_{10}F_{18}$
463.	
464.	
465.	
466.	
467.	$C_{12}F_{17}$
468.	
469.	C_9F_{19}
470.	
471.	
472.	
473.	
474.	$C_{11}F_{18}$

m/e	Ion
475.	
476.	
477.	
478.	
479.	
480.	
481.	$C_{10}F_{19}$
482.	
483.	
484.	
485.	
486.	$C_{12}F_{18}$
487.	
488.	
489.	
490.	
491.	
492.	
493.	$C_{11}F_{19}$

m/e	Ion
494.	
495.	
496.	
497.	
498.	
499.	
500.	
501.	
502.	
503.	
504.	
505.	$C_{12}F_{19}$
506.	
507.	
508.	
509.	
510.	
511.	
512.	$C_{11}F_{20}$

m/e	Ion
513.	
514.	
515.	
516.	
517.	$C_{13}F_{19}$
518.	
519.	
520.	
521.	
522.	
523.	
524.	$C_{12}F_{20}$
525.	
526.	
527.	
528.	
529.	
530.	
531.	$C_{11}F_{21}$

m/e	Ion
532.	
533.	
534.	
535.	
536.	$C_{13}F_{20}$
537.	
538.	
539.	
540.	
541.	
542.	
543.	$C_{12}F_{21}$
544.	
545.	
546.	
547.	
548.	
549.	
550.	

m/e	Ion
551.	
552.	
553.	
554.	
555.	$C_{13}F_{21}$
556.	
557.	
558.	
559.	
560.	
561.	
562.	$C_{12}F_{22}$
563.	
564.	
565.	
566.	
567.	$C_{14}F_{21}$
568.	
569.	

m/e	Ion
570.	
571.	
572.	
573.	
574.	$C_{13}F_{22}$
575.	
576.	
577.	
578.	
579.	
580.	
581.	$C_{12}F_{23}$
582.	
583.	
584.	
585.	
586.	
587.	
588.	

m/e	Ion
589.	
590.	
591.	
592.	
593.	$C_{13}F_{23}$
594.	
595.	
596.	
597.	
598.	
599.	
600.	
605.	$C_{14}F_{23}$
610.	
615.	
617.	$C_{15}F_{23}$

m/e	Ion
620.	
625.	
630.	
631.	$C_{13}F_{25}$
635.	
640.	
643.	$C_{14}F_{25}$
645.	
650.	
655.	
660.	
665.	
670.	
675.	

m/e	Ion
680.	
685.	
690.	
695.	
700.	
705.	
710.	
715.	
720.	
725.	
730.	
735.	

m/e	Ion
740.	
745.	
750.	
755.	
760.	
765.	
770.	
775.	
780.	
785.	
790.	
795.	

m/e	Ion
800.	
825.	
850.	
875.	
900.	
925.	
950.	
975.	
1000.	
1025.	
1050.	
1075.	

m/e	Ion
1100.	
1125.	
1150.	
1175.	
1200.	
1250.	
1300.	
1350.	
1400.	
1450.	
1500.	
1600.	

m/e	Ion
1700.	
1800.	
1900.	
2000.	